Len's Notes

Michael Ettinger

Michael Terence
Publishing

For my wife Angela and my brothers and sisters…

One

Giza Egypt, May 2012

It was four-thirty in the morning when I woke sensing something dreadful had happened. I quickly slipped into my jeans and put on the first tee shirt I could find, not bothering with shoes and socks I made my way to the living room. I switched on the lights and immediately saw my friend Len slumped over his computer desk, his head was twisted to one side, resting at a curious angle on the computers keyboard, his eyes, unmoving staring up to the ceiling.

I managed to get him upright, steadying him as he swayed around in the computer chair. He looked deathly white and his skin was cold to my touch, I frantically tried to find a pulse or any signs of life. I shouted his name.

"Len, it's Henry, answer me."

As I looked at him, I noticed his face seemed out of shape with his mouth twisted open. I looked more closely, he had been sick and his eyes had a vacant look. I eased him back down on to the desk as gently as I could and quickly went over to the phone, dialling the Cairo emergency services. A man saying he was Mohammad took my name, phone number and our address, and then he asked about Len's condition. I told him that I thought Len was dead. From the little I knew about medical conditions, it looked to me like he had died of a brain haemorrhage or perhaps a stroke.

I put the phone back into the cradle and waited for the

ambulance. Whilst I waited I went over and stood beside him as if on guard not knowing what else to do. The ambulance arrived about an hour later, followed by the local police; I gave them a statement and was told not to leave the apartment. The rest of the day became a blur but I remember sometime in the afternoon after a detailed examination of where Len had died, they took his body to the mortuary.

Later in the evening, I rang Len's parents who lived in Richmond close to London England, where the Egyptian Embassy was located. I had never spoken to Len's father before. He was a diplomat at the embassy, his voice sounded cultured, similar to Len's as he answered. He was very calm and polite, thanking me for phoning so quickly, saying that he and Len's Mother would take the next flight from Heathrow to Cairo and would I stay at the flat until they arrived. Of course, I agreed but in the meantime, I found I couldn't eat or sleep, I just sat on the bed in my room, numb with shock, Len Balthazar had been my best friend.

His parents arrived later the next day, they were what you might describe as dignified, nice, very polite, you could tell Len's father was a diplomat, after enquiring over my own wellbeing he thanked me for everything I had done. Len's father spent some time looking at Len's work on the laptop. Before they left for the mortuary, he asked if I would complete his son's work, saying how important it was and that once complete he would get it published, adding that I was welcome to stay on at the flat. It was more of a polite command than a request, perhaps I should have given the request more thought but I found myself readily agreeing, then a week later they were gone taking Len's body back to Richmond in Surrey where he was to be buried and would I contact them in the coming weeks on the progress of the book. I said yes, but in reality, I did not know where to start.

Another week passed before I gathered and assembled the papers, diary and journals lying beside Len's computer, mixed into heaps and masses of paper, was the first draft of his notes on the nature of the Universe; the importance of Mathematics and where did we come from, natural evolution or creationism, they were the only interests in his life.

The task now was to check the computer printouts against his handwritten notes, put them in some order and get the salient points into an orderly format, but where to begin?

I picked up one of many exercise books, reading the notes brought back many fond memories of our brief friendship but they didn't make my task any easier, Len was dead, just twenty-six years of age, I had known him for a mere nine months, but inside I felt I had known him all my life, I began working on the book developed from Len's papers and computerised notes, his diary, some recollections of my life in Arizona, recollections of Len and the main issue, mankind's evolution and destiny.

Len had told me that ever since his sixth birthday when his father gave him his first telescope; he had been fascinated by the stars in the night sky. He told me that most nights as a young boy he would spend his time looking through the telescope, sometimes his father would join him and identify the major stars and planets. On his fourteenth birthday his father gave him a much larger telescope, some books and charts of the Universe.

Len said. *"Studying the Universe was like entering another world, a world of magic and awe-inspiring wonder that I never tired of."*

Len was brought up as a Catholic at his mother's insistence, though his father originally a Muslim had become an atheist but wisely didn't broadcast his beliefs. As Len grew older he became convinced that somewhere in the Universe a God resided. He had read about Sirius as being the resting place of the Egyptian Pharaohs, he needed to be sure and spent many hours reviewing ancient Egyptian history and studying 'The book of the dead' for answers.

Like his father Len kept his thoughts about belief in God to himself, until he travelled to Egypt to study at the University in Cairo and began getting his thoughts down on paper, the first twenty-five years of his short life had been spent living in Richmond, England with his parents, there were no brothers or sisters he grew up as an only child, very shy, withdrawn, he was self-taught and had a brilliant mind.

Two

When Len first spoke of his beliefs it would have been about nine months earlier September 2011, Len said his initial research reinforced his belief in creationism. Later his views began to change and hovered between Creationism and that of Natural Evolution.

It didn't seem so long ago as I began working on the book; with some trepidation, transferring the information from his exercise books and numerous pieces of paper scattered everywhere in the flat, on to the computer. For clarity I had decided that Len's words whether written or spoken would be shown in italics in the book. Below are some of his thoughts on the nature of the universe.

Trillions of miles in area, made up mainly of vast areas of empty space, peppered with hundreds of galaxies and billions of stars, gases and dust, even with the most powerful of telescopes we can only see a fraction of the Universe. I believe it is too huge to properly contemplate and what we can't see behind those twinkling stars is left to our imagination.

No matter, this hasn't stopped a whole raft of academics, scientists and mathematicians intensifying their research and theories on how the Universe was created, when and how the Earth was formed, some astronomers' claiming that there are some 200 billion stars alone in the Milky Way and many more in an ever-expanding and possibly flat Universe, populated with, strings, super strings, black holes, worm holes, dark energy and dark matter. The Universes size is measured in 'light years' and is said to be 13.5 billion years old. My research runs in tandem with the ever-growing investigation on the origin of mankind.

Were we created in God's image as described in the Christian bible some six to eight thousand years ago? Or did we evolve from the chimpanzee around one hundred thousand years ago following the formation of the Sun and the tiny planet Earth some 4.543 billion years earlier?

Paul Gauguin's famous painting questions, 'D'Ou Venons nous? Que Sommes Nous? Qu Allons Nous?" Where do we come from? What are we? Where are we going? Prompted me to review Charles Darwin's theory of the evolution of mankind and the raft of scientific evidence supporting the 'big bang' theory that created the Universe.

I turned the page fascinated; most of the notes had been underlined with various scribbles in the margins, Len had written:

Scientists quite rightly, insist on 'hard' factual answers to the elusive questions life poses; more so today, with computers and computer modelling to hand, providing many of the answers. The computer models undertake the leg work of research; in many cases establish the findings in a way that Scientists could never undertake on their own. The prospect of any Scientist being able to check by hand the billions of calculations churned out by computers, relating to the size, shape, age and number of stars in the Universe is simply not credible.

Len suspected many current scientific claims were purely theoretical, based mainly on research and data provided by computers, leaving the Scientists alarmingly detached from his own research, to become the observer and technical assistant to the computer, Len had written:

I suggest more often than not, the Scientist has no way of verifying the information or understanding the complexity of the computer models created by the Programmers. The reality is that computers used badly or relied upon too much become too big and powerful to manage and worryingly they have also become a tool Scientists cannot do without, with each new development in computer and digital technology the Scientist finds himself further detached, marginalised from his own research and beliefs.

Moving on Len had noted.

The questions and doubts surrounding the Biblical records that claimed God created the Earth had until Copernicus and Galileo's time remained unchallenged on a technical basis. Galileo's crushing statement confirming Copernicus's finding in the 15th century that the Earth orbited the Sun and was a globe, not a flat surface, was a turning point for those who doubted God had created the Garden of Eden, Adam and Eve as recorded in the bible.

Galileo's pronouncements shook the Christian establishment to its core. Worse was to come, three centuries later, when Charles Darwin and Alfred Wallace proclaimed that humans had evolved directly from the chimpanzee as part of natural evolution.

It gave the scientists who doubted a 'godly' involvement in the creation of mankind, the ammunition they needed to challenge and shoot down what they saw as the Bibles naive view of God creating the Universe in six days then resting on the seventh.

The scientific research supporting natural evolution as the origin of the Universe and life on earth provides for many people a clear, step by step, factual platform as to how mankind evolved. Its logic and reasoning are easy to grasp, compelling and difficult to dismiss. By the middle of the twentieth century, 'God' as the creator of the Universe has been debunked by many in the scientific community and replaced with the 'Big Bang' theory rejected but labelled as such by Sir Fredrick Hoyle in 1950 in a radio broadcast for the BBC, Hoyle had also written a book 'The nature of the Universe'.

Len went on to say:

"When challenging myself for tangible proof, I considered the 'big bang' theory to be equally frail as the theory of creationism."

And:

"Steven Hawking the most eminent scientist of our day may have been right to suggest 'the Universe was created from a singularity' but it begs the question. If this were so the singularities origin would have been a collapsed star, had this been the case, the collapsed star must surely have already been contained within an existing Universe, so where does that leave us?

Concerning the time element quoted in the Bible, that God created the Universe in six days, we can deduce that the time element (six days) may not have been measured in the days we count with each revolution of the earth on its axis, God may have said, he created the Universe in six days, perhaps each 'God day' was the time the newly created Universe took to revolve around his Kingdom. This would allow the claim of six days to have merit and resolve this anomaly. If this is the case it will bring some comfort to the creationist and irritation to the atheists who go along with the big bang theory of the universe being created in milliseconds, thirteen and a half billion years ago making God's six-day creation look rather slow. Both scientific and theological claims on the origin of the Universe and life on Earth have fundamental questions which I believe can never be properly answered by science alone. In the end it comes down to an individuals' belief, though I suggest both creationism and natural evolution might run parallel to each other rather than one being wholly wrong and the other wholly right."

Len and I would discuss these issues long into the night in the flat we shared, finding ourselves mainly in agreement that there was 'something missing' in the science of natural evolution, wanting answers to questions raised regarding the Big Bang theory prompted us, as his suggestion to pool our ideas and set out our findings in a thesis, I may add Len was being very generous in the said pooling of our ideas, 99% of which were his. In truth I was the leg man and happy with my role, keeping records and

Len on an even keel.

Len was fired up, the aim he said is to show that the science supporting man's natural evolution as described by Charles Darwin and Alfred Wallace, though not disputed is not the whole story of mankind and that natural evolution can run side by side with Christian belief of creationism, that God created man in his own image, Len had noted in his diary on the eleventh of May 2011.

A contradiction in terms you may think, but the link between natural evolution and a godly creation of mankind can be tenuously made by reference to 'Savants' a very rare group of people who have populated the world over the centuries, astonishing their contemporaries of the time with their supernatural powers.

Further research led Len to consider that Savants in many ways mirrored the 'elusive something' deep within all of us that defies logical explanation and cannot be described by science or quantified by mathematics as a provable equation. I found more notes on the subject but not on his laptop.

I acknowledge that on its own, the bold statement, God created the Universe and everything in it in six days, seems very unlikely when challenged by science. One obvious question scientists would ask is where does Einstein's theory of relativity fit in. Oddly enough Einstein who gave us the theory of relativity also enjoyed and retained his belief in life after death, but then, who am I to question one of the greatest minds of the twentieth century. Replacing one set of beliefs with another which are profoundly different is one thing but I question, just how sound is the science that seeks to replace God as the creator of the Universe with the Big Bang theory? A science that states there is no life other than the particles of matter that have evolved in a timeless and ever-expanding Universe billions of years old. That there is no God, the Universe and all within it are no more than a mixture of random atoms, elements as identified and listed by the periodic table. Inert gases formed into living organisms and that we 'human beings 'are merely matter, there is no soul that following our physical death, neither do we traverse the heavens to enjoy a second life with the eternal father, the supreme being.

I suggest that in any event, creationism played the first and major part in the formation of our Universe and also acknowledge that the Earth we inhabit is a tiny part of the Universe and that natural evolution also played a part in a created Universe as mankind's destiny unfolds through time. It's worth noting that Alpha Centauri A and Alpha Centauri B, the nearest stars to Earth are said to be a mere 4.2 light-years from earth or converted to miles about 25.2 trillion miles from Earth. Space travel even to this closest star would seem to be out of reach, taking anything between 100 and 900 years to reach the destination if ever! Equally I find it difficult to believe that someone, an alien pointing a giant telescope towards the Sun from either Alpha Centauri A or B would be able to detect our tiny planet, a mere 7.926 miles in diameter that has no light of its own, when in front of the Sun in its yearly orbit nothing more than a dim halo.

The problem for the Academic and Scientist, Len had written:

Creationism can never be set down as a provable equation much like Einstein's theory of relativity. What is the mass of the soul? What does it look like and why can't we see it, the Scientists ask! There are various suggestions but no complete agreement as to how old the Universe might be. Researching the Web and Science Journals we read that the Universe is somewhere between 8 to 20 billion years old, with John Hurchra claiming some time ago, it was definitely 9 billion years old. It is widely believed by many Scientists that the Universe 'a singularity' was formed in one sudden burst of energy releasing an immensely dense ball of energy and matter over 10,000 degrees Fahrenheit, into space, which we call the Universe 13.5 billion years ago. But, I ask! What did the Universe burst into? And what surrounds and contains our expanding Universe, another Universe?

Scientists have no clear answers to this question, nor can they. We are asked to accept these events 'the big bang' occurred in the first millionth of the first second of the creation of the Universe. Not satisfied with these mind-blowing facts Scientists and Cosmologists followed up by telling us the Universe could be flat rather than spherical and that it is still expanding and that light is pear-shaped, making the calculation of distance between objects in space accurately, more complex to say the least.

I could see by Len's jerky handwriting that some of the concepts surrounding the origin of the Universe had made him angry, in spiky writing, he had written:

To make matters more confusing for ordinary folk, another school of Scientists dispute that the Universe is still expanding, namely the 'steady-state theorists' who agreed with the big bang concept, but say the Universe has stopped expanding, though neither group can tell you with any certainty what the universe expanded into. Then there is the 'big crunch' theorists who believe that sometime in the future, the Universe will get brighter and hotter until it eventually implodes and is crunched out of existence becoming what is termed a singularity. What happens to the space surrounding the Universe after the big crunch also remains unanswered. The Scientists of the 20th century were split on this issue of the 'steady-state theory' as opposed to an 'expanding universe' (now favoured as the most plausible explanation of the existence of the Universe by the scientific community), with Einstein somewhere in the middle of the debate and Stephen Hawking leading the way on the theory of an expanding Universe.

In CERN, Geneva, a group of scientists is looking for the 'God particle' in a giant accelerator collider some 26 miles in circumference built underground which is designed to simulate the same conditions as those of the big bang.

Three hundred years earlier the colossus of mathematics Isaac

Newton working alone his laboratory was also searching for the 'god particle' using alchemy rather than a giant accelerator to confirm his theory. Newton's understanding of the Universe was way ahead of his time, his knowledge and theories came from the study of ancient teachings and manuscripts, he had like many other alchemists translated 'The Emerald Tablet' an ancient script written in Arabic that was said to hold the secrets of the Universe and some claim dates back to 36,000 BC, the tablets also makes reference to the fabled Atlantis. Newton was a lone pioneer that fitted into the role of genius or savant with perfect ease. Sadly he let himself down in later life, a new ugly side of his character revealed, perhaps it was the handling of lead, mercury and other poisonous substances that he may have ingested, inhaled that altered his mind that created his callous regard and spite towards his fellow scientists. It was a sad end to one of the greatest mathematicians of any age. Sir Isaac Newton is a hero of mine, if I had one-tenth of his ability I would be the happiest of men, to walk in his shadow would be an honour.

That was Len, wearing his heart on his sleeve, unafraid, he liked to nail his beliefs to the cross, smiling I read more.

Newton would have known, there's a huge difference between a series of tiny controlled scientific experiments undertaken within a computer programmed accelerator than that of the 'big bang' where trillions of particles exploded outwards in every direction in a matter of milliseconds, at colossal temperatures covering trillions of miles to form the Universe. Scientists it seems cannot tell us just what the Universe is expanding into; perhaps a new 'Special Special Theory of Relativity' is needed to answer this question or more simply a belief in God, as the creator of all things.

The more Len researched, the more uncomfortable he became with the claims that were being made in the name of Science, often presented as solid facts. What concerned Len so much, were that many claims which came into the public domain, usually through televised programs, often remaining unchallenged or have not been properly substantiated in any meaningful way for the non-scientifically minded to understand. Potentially more worrying, fundamental questions relating to the laws of science seemed to have been conveniently forgotten, ignored or re-moulded to fit the theory of the day.

"To put it into perspective."

Len had said one evening after a long discussion on the number of stars in the Universe.

"The following observations Henry, illustrate just how 'big' the numbers are that we are dealing with, for example: If a Scientist wanted to attempt to verify the number of constantly moving stars in the Milky Way. For the purpose of argument, let's say he was able to count, plot and record 1 star every three seconds then! In one minute he would have counted 20 stars after an hour he would have counted 1200 stars, in one 10-hour working day (without a break) he would have counted 12,000 stars. In one year working every day of the year he would have counted 4,380,000 stars, and in a lifetime spanning say 70 years counting from the moment of his birth, counting for 10 hours every day he would have only counted 306,600,000 stars. To count, plot and record 200 billion stars in the Milky Way the Scientist would have to have lived 652 years, counting stars every day without a break, it's worth noting that our solar system is moving around the milky way at 514,000 miles per hour."

Len was laughing, something he rarely did when discussing Science, saying. *"The computer programmers located in the American Museum of Natural History with the aid of their computers and digital mapping technology would take much less time to count plot and record the stars than the lone scientist but the programmers have no way of knowing if their digital information is completely accurate. Checking and auditing computer print outs manually would take just as long as counting the stars in the first place, that's if someone could live that long or be bothered to undertake the task."*

I stopped taking notes and looked at Len, a questioning grin on my face.

"Does this mean the science is wrong Len?" I asked playfully.

Len stopped laughing and for a moment looked serious again.

"No Henry, it just means that the Big Bang theorists, along with Cosmologists who predict the number of stars in the Universe, have the same status as the authors of the Bible who recorded that 'the Universe, the Earth and mankind was created in six days by God. In reality Henry for all their research Scientists are unable to provide answers to basic questions in any greater depth than the theologians that they despise."

Len was clearly enjoying himself, later in the evening, several ideas had come together and crystallised in his mind, he added.

"In both camps as of this moment in time Henry, it comes down to what one believes, not what or how much anyone knows. Belief is essential, the lifeblood and the fuel that drives Scientists and Theologians on, without belief they would stop. But the claims they dangle in front of us as truths are one thing Henry, proof in all its glory and pure absolutes, rock hard substances, polished shiny surfaces, truths that sparkle like diamonds are elusive and not so easily found."

When I went to bed that night my mind was teeming with ideas, the thought of a lone Scientist, mapping and counting the billions of stars filling the Universe, of God reaching down from some unknown place, a ball of clay in his hands, forming the Garden of Eden and moulding two tiny figures, Adam and Eve. My head was pounding, exhausted, laying on the bed, I found myself recalling the first time I had visited an Observatory. It was June 10th 1996, I was ten years old; the school I attended arranged a bus trip to the Lowell Observatory in Flagstaff Arizona, not so far from where we lived. My father Bald Eagle was initially opposed to my going but relented two days before the planned visit. It was a life-changing experience for me much to my father's annoyance. When I got back home he was standing at the entrance to his tepee waiting for me, my mother hovering around the vegetable garden.

"So little Red Feather," he said smiling, "You've seen the Universe through the white man's big eyes?" I didn't reply.

"What did you see? Your ancestor's souls travelling through space? The spirit of the Indian Warrior, The death of mankind?"

Mocking me, my father laughed, his hands raised into the air, pointing but at what?

"It was good father; I saw Jupiter and 'The Great Bear." I offered in reply.

"Great bear, my foot, is that what the white man teaches you at school? Your place is here in the land of our forefathers, to look after your brothers and sisters when I am gone, not spending your time in the white man's schools and towns the white man has created, if he knew anything he would know looking through a telescope, however big wouldn't tell him anything we native Americans don't already know.

The white men are clowns." I wanted to answer him with some thoughts I had come up with but my mother called over saying my dinner was ready. I made my way past her, my father stood unmoving staring across the plains towards the mountains his hand raised to shield his eyes from the blazing sun. We never spoke again about the trip to Lowell or my interest in astronomy. I eventually fell asleep, dreaming of the Great Bear. Fifteen years on and the visit to Lowell now a distant memory, a new day, Len was ready to go again, I suspected he had been up all night, over breakfast I was proved right when he said.

"Going on from where we left off last night Henry, I've worked out that to catalogue 200 billion stars in the Milky Way alone with a simple grid and reference number at the rate of say, 60 lines per page would fill 3.3 billion pages. Split into numerical volumes for reference, each volume containing 450 pages there would be some 7,407,407 books, Seven and a half million books Henry!"

Len stood up, his hands thrust into the pockets of the ragged grey cardigan he liked to wear. He looked at me with some satisfaction.

"That's a lot of books Len," I replied, my head was still churning from all the data it had been subjected to the night before, I needed a break saying.

"I'm going for a walk Len." As I reached the door Len shouted.

"Henry, if you managed to review say one book every day for the whole of your life you would be over 2,000 years old when you put the last volume down."

He laughed again adding. *"I also worked out that the smallest map laid flat, showing 200 billion stars side by side to a scale where you could see them properly in relation to each other, would be around 450 Metres square and that's just the milky way."*

I blinked as I stood in the morning sunlight, Len was jumping around like a kid with a new toy, me! I was bushed.

"A big piece of paper Len," I said trying to close the

door.

"Another thing Henry, I worked out that if each book was 50mm wide, the shelf length required to house them all would be 370,000 Metres. If you stacked the books on shelves say 7 shelves deep you would need a building 210 Metres long by 250 Meters wide to house them all."

I wanted to answer, to say, Len they don't store data in that way any more; they use Cloud, CDs and other IT devices. I knew what Len's reply would be.

The extent of the digital information viewed on a television, laptop or computer screen is not able to convey the information meaningfully and is out of context with the big picture, that's why I prefer books.

It was a point I fully agreed with. Len thought that looking at data on a computer screen was not the same as having a book or a map in your hands, it's too remote. It can't be seen or felt, touched and sensed as a whole and the potential to miss something or for something to get lost in the viewing of information on a computer screen, to my mind the traditional form of reviewing information in books and on paper is much more fulfilling. I wondered, perhaps somewhere in America there is a building that houses 7,500 volumes cataloguing the 200,000,000 stars inhabiting the Milky Way and another huge building housing the stars in other parts of the universe, though I doubted it.

To Len's mind, the danger in scientific-based research, such as the 'big bang theory' was that many people who have grown up in the computer industry believe that they don't need in-depth research or books when they have computers which does it all for them. Sometimes Len got up a head of steam, angrily he had scrawled on a piece of paper, that pseudo documentaries and films full of computerised simulation of time travel and the creation of the Universe, black holes that fill our television screens, are presented as factual information. I turned to wave but Len was already back in his chair, staring into the computer screen. It wasn't that I was losing interest; I just couldn't keep pace with Len's relentless pursuit of information and his mercurial mind. He seemed to change direction from one topic to another effortlessly.

With each new day Len moved forward with more thoughts and ideas, he was the driving force of the research; I was happy enough as the pen pusher and record keeper.

Three

We didn't live on a reservation but a homestead equally distant between Flagstaff and Holbrook towards the eastern borders of Arizona and New Mexico which my father had been given by John Cassidy a ranger, it extended to over one hundred acres. Several years later, when I was old enough to understand my mother told me the story of what happened in April 1984, two years before I came into the world. She and my father were driving along route 66, from Flagstaff towards Holbrook and the Apache Death Caves and the Sit Graves National Forest in an old VW camper van which served as their home, my father refusing to live on a reservation. Like all Indians my father had a keen sense of hearing and recognised the sound of a bear growling as it roamed backwards and forwards across the front of a house set back some fifty yards from the road, the bear sounded hungry. Then the bear seeing an old man began to chase after him. Cassidy crippled and hobbling for his life pushed against the door to the house trying to get away from the bear.

My father pulled over and stopped the van on the yard at the front of the house and followed the black bear into the house. By then the old man was pinned against the wall of the living room whimpering, with the bear standing on his two back legs, growling and pawing at him. My father withdrew his hunting knife and attacked the bear from behind but not before it had broken Cassidy's arm with its vicious sweeping paws. Unsurprisingly the bear was hungry after a long winter of hibernation and without food.

Foolishly Cassidy had hung out a white-tailed deer he had killed the day before to bleed out in the barn to the side of the house.

Like all rangers, Cassidy knew black bears had a keen sense of smell and would always come in the direction of the smell of blood sensing a meal was to hand. Time passed and Cassidy had forgotten about black bears and made things worse, by still wearing his butcher's apron which was covered in the deer's blood. In the bear's mind, the deer could wait, there were two meals to be had, he'd start with the old man.

My father drove the knife deep into the bear's neck, it turned and howled and tried to set about my father who had leapt onto its back and was now frantically stabbing the bear in the chest. After what seemed several minutes but in truth was only a minute or so the bear turned again, shaking my father to the floor and limped back out of the house to seek refuge in the fields behind the house.

My father uninjured was joined by my mother who helped Cassidy to his bed where she made a splint for his broken arm. It was clear to my mother and father, that the old man couldn't be left alone; the bear might return at any time and finish him off. It turned out that John Cassidy lived alone, he was seventy-two years old and seen better days, there was no family. My father wasted no time and went out in search of the bear. He tracked it to a creek a mile away, the bear was dead, bled through. The next day my father went back and skinned the bear; the hide still sits on the floor in what was John Cassidy's house. John Cassidy had escaped a very painful death, from being eaten alive. He invited my mother and father to stay at the homestead, saying my father had saved his life and by way of gratitude wanted to leave his home, which had been in his family since 1872, to my father when the time came.

At any other time my father would have left as soon as the old man was well, but Cassidy's generosity was too good to miss and my mother and father spent the next three years looking after him, it was the first white man my father ever liked and the last, there was a mutual admiration and bond between the two men, whilst my mother was like a daughter to him. John Cassidy was as good as his word and made over the homestead to my Father, he died peacefully in his sleep and was buried by my father down by the creek close to where the bear had been buried. It was not long before other Indians; many cousins of my parents joined them on the homestead. It was hard work living off the land with ten families to feed, thirty-three Indians, which included nine children of different ages. The land which was now known as 'Black Bear Ranch' belonged to my father, he was a fiercely proud man and had become a bit of a celebrity for his courage and was respected by Indians and white people alike. He lived in a tepee rather than the house and had always expected me to live the Native American Indian way; he had no time for the white men or their way of life, other than John Cassidy, it was a nice story and made me smile.

However my father's anger was only partly diminished, he told me of how his great, great grandfather and his family had been driven off their land two hundred miles east of where they now lived, still burned deeply inside him. Living on a reservation was never an option, he considered it demeaning. He was a proud man, a warrior and it was clear to me that I fell way short of what he expected of his only son. In my way, I was a warrior too but one that didn't fight or intimidate others, I preferred to pow-wow, though I could be as stubborn as him. My mother was more sympathetic to my needs and with patience and guile persuaded my father to allow me to go to the local school and then on to college, telling my father my destiny should be in my hands and not his. She had also said that if I was to lead our people surrounded by white Americans it was essential I went to their schools, understood their ways to get the best for our people.

Cassidy had left my mother a sum of money in trust for my further education as a thank you for how she had looked after him at the homestead. It was just as well as the UNI was fee-paying. I had opted to take a degree in anthropology, a popular course. UNI was in itself an education with students, professors and teachers from every state and many from other countries, I enjoyed the cosmopolitan air and mixing with people of so many different cultures.

Deep down my father knew my mother was right and reluctantly agreed to my attending the local school and later Phoenix University, but in return said I was to spend an equal amount of time learning and carrying out Indian traditions at the homestead. That was fine by me I loved my heritage, my brothers and sisters and the Indian way of living. I had been named Red Feather by my father who had found a red feather from an American Kestrel outside the tepee on the day of my birth, the birds, a pair had nested close by the homestead. Kestrels were not a bird not often seen in Arizona but one that my father had long admired. The addition 'Henry' to my name was added when I began my studies at UNI in 2008. My father would not have been pleased had he heard me being referred to as Henry, but I didn't mind. it made me feel that I belonged and had been accepted, fellow students told me I was respected and well-liked for my easy-going nature which I guessed I had inherited from my mother Falling Leaves. It was important to me that I could study in a relaxed atmosphere, there were many derogatory names they could have called me, Henry was fine and apparently the name was chosen by some astute fellow students because they said, I looked a lot like Henry Fonda the famous film actor, very flattering. It was a good job my parents didn't visit UNI. I enjoy studying anthropology and sharing the white man's ways and the knowledge gained at university but there was a down side, I soon found out that there were several peer groups at UNI, some that delighted in elitism not my bag, my aim was to keep my head down and blend in, I didn't bite when derogatory comments and name calling came my way. Sadly it was the unfortunate students that fought back that became the food and drink of peer pressure groups. I kept well out of their way until one day after class I watched Pedro Sanchez a student in our class, 4 foot 9 tall, around 7 stone 7 wet through, became the punch bag for John Ellis's Chaves, a name he had borrowed from a Londoner he had met in NY and suited his peer group that enjoyed terrorising both students and teachers alike. Ellis's father was a benefactor of the University, and a big name in Phoenix owning the largest transport and Logistics Company in the south western states, so a lot of ugly behaviour went unreported. I never courted trouble but for some reason I couldn't just walk by, I caught Ellis looking at me, probably seeing me as his next meal. Smiling I went up to him and said, "Hello." he laughed a hungry grin on his face. I held out my hand as if to shake but pulled my hand back at the last minute gripped his fingers between the palm and thumb of my hand, creating a vice like grip, I squeezed his fingers steadily with all my might, we both heard the bones crunching. Smiling I didn't have to say anything I waited a further minute or so until Ellis's smile became a grimace, "Ok that's enough."

he said to the group still messing with Pedro. I let go of his hand and whispered in his ear what would happen, if he messed with Pedro again. I guessed two broken fingers; he wouldn't be writing letters for a while. I was lucky taking out Ellis the peer leader was like putting out a fire that had become starved of oxygen. Nothing further was ever said to me, I had the odd stare, the word in some quarters was that my father was a witch doctor, that I could cast spells and it was best to stay clear of me. The group I mixed with were much gentler and focused on their studies, they were known as the Saint's, aptly named, though I wasn't claiming to be one. Standing up to Ellis was the first and only time I had displayed physical aggression to another human being. It was out of character and very foolish. In truth, I wasn't much of a brave. However, I was utterly thrilled when two years later I learned I had graduated with honours. Seeing me in a cap and gown and being referred to as Doctor Red Feather was too much for my father to take, but my mother and Shining Eyes came to the graduation ceremony. It was all very low key when we returned home, there was no point agitating my father, I admit to having felt proud at the time, I had achieved something my white friends respected, in years to come its status would be invaluable to me when discussing and maintaining Indian rights at our homestead. The icing on the cake was when Shining eyes gave me a graduation gift, a fountain pen with my name, Doctor Red Feather engraved on the pen case.

In reality, I was between two cultures, I detested arguments and it was the main reason I took up the offer to study in Egypt in the summer of 2011 after I had graduated. My father's efforts to ensure I stayed at the homestead had backfired and I left the handful of Indians my uncles, aunts and cousins living on the homestead for an unforgettable adventure in a land I had only read about in books. But my father would have the last word. "You will come back home soon Red Feather; you don't belong with the white man."

I nodded sheepishly, I wanted to part on good terms without bad words between us. "But don't leave it too long Red Feather, you're needed here." It was a command
I found myself saying, "Yes father," as he turned and entered the tepee, leaving me with no goodbye. I made my way alone to the Phoenix Sky Harbour International Airport to catch my plane to Alexandria in Egypt.

Four

Arizona

Until I met Len, 'big numbers' weren't something I spent a lot of time thinking about. From what I had read and my father 'Bald Eagle' had told me between 6 to 9 million Native American Indians had lost their lives in the relentless pursuit of land by the white settlers over a period of 250 years.

Our homestead and the reservations in Arizona along with many others scattered across America collectively amounted to hundreds rather than thousands of native Indians, all that was left of our nation. It was not a figure I liked to dwell on. During my early schooling and then at UNI I had always avoided maths as a subject, preferring Social Science and Anthropology.

The only numbers I was interested in was how fast 'Snow Ridge' galloped the white pony my father allowed me to ride as a boy and then much later how fast was King, my road bike. From the age of ten to twenty I worked in the local gas station Saturdays and Sundays for Lester Boyd a tall thin white man in his fifties with a ruddy face and weak voice, he always wore his greasy Mobil overalls and an 'Arizona' snapback baseball cap. Lester was a decent man and took a liking to me for some reason, always greeting me with a smile; he called me 'Red Henry'. His own boys, Billy and Jed, were 3 and 4 years older than me couldn't hack it, they would sit on the veranda, sullen faced watching me stacking the cans of oil, shelf-filling, tidying and sweeping the forecourt when there was no one to serve. It was hard work in the merciless Arizona heat but I had a plan.

All the nickels, dimes and dollars I earned, went into a box I kept under my bed. After ten years I figured I had saved enough. One day to my father's horror I came home, riding an old Harley Davidson 'Road King' I had brought for $900 from Lester's cousin Clyde Walker with the money I had saved.

I can remember the day Clyde handed over the bike, jangling the bikes keys.

"You mind you look after King Red Feather," he said handing me the keys, adding.

"King was my best friend since."

I could see the tears well up in his eyes, as he wiped the sweat from his brow, I had an idea how he was feeling.

"Keep King polished and shiny and new like I have all these years Red."

"I will Mr Walker," I said, feeling embarrassed; Lester kept walking across the forecourt, his head down keeping busy, Billy and Jed sitting on the wall as usual, looking pensive with an ugly smirk on their faces. I shook My Walkers hand promising to take care of King.

"And another thing," he said as I was walking over to the bike ready for my first ride, I stood and turned. "Yes, Mr Walker."

"Don't be a stranger Red Feather, now you have King."

"No Sir." I sat on the bike and inserted the key; there were two kings that day, one was my bike King, the other was me. I felt so good I was a King, a dream had come true. I gently let out the throttle and eased King into motion, gliding up the road for a couple of miles as smooth as could be and back to the garage. Lester had said I could keep King round the back in the store until I was ready to take the bike home. It didn't end there, a couple of days later Clyde turned up with his easy smile, offering to teach me to ride, with his patience and tuition I learned to ride on route 66 and passing my test before taking King home.

Had I fallen off of the bike, which Billy and Jed were willing me to do, that would have ended my biking. Clyde told me he had broken his ankle following a bad fall on King, hence the sale, I knew this but had said nothing, one thing for sure, I didn't want to end up the same way or give my father the opportunity of banning me from riding the bike. A few weeks later I took King home, my father was furious and for a short while it was a sore subject between us, with my mother keeping out of sight whenever the subject came up. It amused me that however brave my father was, and he was a brave man, he always declined to ride King. When I offered he would just scowl and either change the subject or find something to do. After a two week standoff and my mentioning that King took me to and from the University in Phoenix, my father relented and I was allowed to keep King.

As well as my travelling on route 66 through Oatman to the west coast of America and Los Angeles, King diligently took me back and forth to the University in Phoenix for four years, King was my greatest companion. The sensation of riding King was pure bliss, a feeling of total freedom, it was as if there was a bond between King's handlebars and my gloved hands, my thighs gripping King body as the sound of the engine vibrated through every bone in my body, my head buzzing till we merged into one being. What a feeling, for four years we were inseparable.

Watching the rev counter as it hovered on red and the speedometer flickering around 110 mph as I raced through the gears were the only numbers that I recall with any real affection. One day coming back from Phoenix I stopped at a gas station to fill up. Close to their Phoenix headquarters, there were a group of Hells Angel bikers parked up on the forecourt, they looked over as I drew up, I nodded politely as I went into the shop. As I came out a guy with long red hair in a ponytail, black leathers, with muscular arms covered in tattoo's walked over, he looked the real McCoy. I hoped this wasn't going to be trouble, I needn't have worried he greeted me with a smile. "The names Chainsaw, though some people call me Red, as in Red Devil, I like your bike man," he said as I walked back to King.

"Yes," I said, "King's a great ride."

"I didn't catch your name, feller, don't suppose you want to sell her? I have 1,000 bucks here."

He patted a wad of notes which were in his top pocket, a slow smile formed on his face. I wasn't sure exactly what to say, I figured the smile could easily become a frown if I said the wrong thing, I nodded in acknowledgement.

"It's, Red Feather, Henry Red Feather." I offered him my hand. "Glad to meet you Chainsaw." The smile remained as he patted the money again.

"Red, how cool, having the same name kinda makes us brothers." There was a moment's silence as he continued to inspect the bike. "It's a FLHRSI Harley with V2 4-stroke fuel injection; I could push to eleven hundred if it helps Red."

Breathing a sigh of relief, I found myself staring at Chainsaws gold-capped teeth as his smile broadened.

"It's a great offer Chainsaw, any other time I would be glad to accept your offer but I need King to get me back and forth to Phoenix Uni." He nodded as if understanding, still wearing the smile. "Well, if you ever change your mind Red."

It was my turn to smile, we spoke a little more about bikes, exchanging stats on various models and then someone called over to him and he started to walk back to his friends, his hand raised giving a friendly wave, I waved back and gunned King, as I was about to set off he shouted. "Hey Red, there's always a place in the Chapter for guys who cherish their bikes." The smile was still there, I nodded and did a sought of salute with my right hand, saying

"Thanks, Chainsaw, I'm really honoured," as I drove off. On the way home I thought about the episode, I was ashamed that I had pre-judged Chainsaw thinking that he might have robbed me, taken the bike or worse done me in. I'm not sure how Chainsaw got his grisly sounding name, but he treated me right and knew everything there was to know about bikes. I came to the conclusion that there were worse things than being a member of the Hells Angels Phoenix Chapter, not everybody's cup of tea but like my Indian brothers they were in a minority in a big country seeking freedom and like any group of people there were good and bad. My father always said.

"Look beneath the surface Red Feather, that's where you'll find the real man, black, white red or yellow, colour doesn't matter, it's what's inside that counts."

In his way Chainsaw and the other members of the Chapter were warriors, fierce, loyal and loving to those of their kind, defending their freedom. That we had in common, I think my father would have been in a Chapter had he been a white man but not me, I was more of a loner, King was the only friend I had. Now Kings parked up in a disused shed at the reservation, my father thinks he has the only key but I have a spare. The next time I ride King, I will set off East along 66, taking me to Missouri, Kansas to Illinois and finally Chicago, the windy city, places I've only read and dreamed about.

Cairo, Egypt

My dissertation at UNI was on the Aztec Civilisation, which led me to want to study Egyptology. When a place came up at Cairo's University in Egypt to study the Egyptian Civilisations, it was too good to miss; I applied for a place expecting everything to turn out perfectly, it didn't happen that way. I had a run-in with Professor Dougall McDonald a dower Scotsman, who took the Anthropology session. I quickly found out he had an in-built dislike for anyone who wasn't Scottish. It was also where I met Len; we were in the same class. As well as not being Scottish I had the misfortune to present my first essay (of choice) on Ronald Laing the famous Scottish Psychiatrist of the nineteen sixties who changed the perception of mental illness. Someone it turned out McDonald loathed, which was compounded by my second paper (of choice), relating to Carlos Castaneda and his series of Books 'The teachings of Don Juan', a native American Indian who was also a Sharman, I quickly found out that Castaneda was equally disliked by McDonald telling everyone in the class, Castaneda was a fraud and my paper was not worthy of being marked. McDonald's face became the colour of a ripe tomato when pointing his finger at me like an inmate from an asylum he screamed, the 'Teachings of Don Juan' was Mumbo Jumbo, forbidding anyone else to read it. My father would have hit McDonald just once, hard enough to knock him out had the words been directed at him, to my shame I sat silently in the class taking it when I should have got up and left, the consolation was that I would not have made friends with Len. McDonald had guessed rightly that had I quit there would have been letters exchanged by the Phoenix and Cairo Universities, my father would have been told and would have berated me for my behaviour, worse still he would have told Shining eyes I was not worthy of her, I would be a laughing stock and a shadow leader of our small tribe when my father seeded his leadership. It was a no-win situation, I either had to put up or shut up. The dumb Indian, I quickly became McDonald's whipping boy. The shame of what I should have done on that fateful day is embedded in my mind like a bad dream and never leaves me. To make matters worse I had also lost my lodgings in Cairo and was about to give up and return home, when Len suggested we share the flat that his father owned. McDonald for some reason disliked Len almost as much as he disliked me. I suspected in Len's case, McDonald's dislike of Len was one of pure jealousy, it was obvious to me; there was nothing McDonald could teach Len.

Len was unusually tall for an Egyptian, he had a slender angular build, classic Egyptian features, straight black hair, parted to one side and combed down, warm olive/brown colouring, his piercing black eyes missed nothing written in a book or on a blackboard. He had a keen intelligent face, a slightly hooked nose and sculptured lips below a neatly trimmed moustache. He would wear a mixture of old and new clothes which included Savile Row suits, shirts, ties and Church leather brogues contrasted with his Oxford scarf, a tatty grey cardigan and an over large dressing-gown which had seen better days and beaten leather slippers he always wore in the flat. Len told me that he didn't smoke, take drugs, rarely drank and had never had a girlfriend; I put the last of his comments down to his extreme shyness, for that matter neither had I been with a woman, I was always too busy but I had met a woman my age at the homestead, Shining eyes a distant cousin on my mother's side. She was breathtakingly beautiful but self-effacing in her ways, we had smiled and before I left we spoke properly to each other. I said I was going on a course in Egypt for 18 months and I hoped she would understand and would want to see me when I returned. When she said yes, her words and smile nearly stopped me from going. The kiss was my very first kiss with a woman and I can still feel the warmth and softness of her lips. Len was extremely polite, well-mannered and spoke in an educated way, when properly dressed he looked handsome, elegant, the man about town but most of the time, dressed in a mixture of clothes, unshaven, his hair uncombed, the weak smile, he looked dishevelled and much older than his twenty-six years. The shadows around his eyes were a give-a-way of too much work and not enough relaxation, food or sleep. But from the moment we met, I liked Len's self-effacing manner. As well as being remarkably talented, I soon discovered he was generous, kind and had a gentle nature.

We soon became good friends, it was impossible not to admire Len. I began to realise I was probably in the presence of a genius. Like all people with such rare ability, there was a fine line between their brilliance and mental fragility. Len could quickly get upset with himself if things did not turn out how he anticipated. We enjoyed each others company, Len would say, I was a great help in keeping him calm enough to undertake his research. I suspected he was lonely and was glad of my company. I realised that Len had very few friends and apart from the time at home with his parents had never lived with anyone else, though this didn't mean anything to me, it was just an observation, I had been brought up not to judge people I met. My father saying it was disrespectful, to judge people you had only just met, I never really understood what my Father had meant by that until I met Len. Despite my father's warnings about making early judgements, I came to the conclusion that Len was overly intense and very shy; though it didn't stop me liking him. Anyway, Len was not alone I had my own problems, I didn't like to admit it but I had been carrying a chip on my shoulder for a long time. Sometimes I felt I was treated like one of the last remaining dumb Indians, the McDonalds of this world with their scathing criticism didn't help but Len's enthusiasm was contagious, he made me realise how important it was to focus on the big issues, there was too much to do, to dwell on what might have been. I realised that it was time to stop my navel-gazing. By just being there, Len made me want to think outside of myself. I began to find his research exciting, happy to listen to Len and make notes highlighting the points he considered had not been properly addressed relating to the big bang theory. The reality of identifying how many books would be needed to chronicle the number of stars claimed to have been identified in the Milky Way proved to me that those interested in cosmology have to take the huge numbers banded around on trust. The number of questions needing more in-depth answers were too numerous to list. Len ended up refining them down to a handful which he considered fundamental in establishing the soundness of the Big bang theory.

Firstly how the small ball of 'dense matter' said to be responsible for creating the Universe was itself formed prior to the 'big bang', and importantly how old was this dense matter, prior to the 'big bang'? And if it was 'a singularity' where had it come from?

Secondly, prior to the big bang, what was the ball of 'dense matter' contained and what did it explode and expand into? An existing universe, a vacuum, another Universe, or empty space? Could it have exploded into nothing or as some Scientists suggest, just exploded and then expand from within itself!!!

How do these claims fit into Einstein's theory of relativity?

Thirdly Scientists tell us, the newly created Universe reached enormous temperatures in the first milliseconds following the 'big bang'. Where did the energy come from to create such heat in such a short period of time? Wouldn't the enormous temperatures have destroyed the elements and matter following the big bang?

How cold was the space the Universe expanded into in one millisecond in time?

I suggest this information is necessary to measure accurately the initial change in temperature of the Universe.

Fourthly I think crucial, Scientists need to be able to establish the location of the centre of the Universe, where the Big Bang occurred, and its relationship to Earth (said to have formed some 8 billion years later) if scientists are to plot the billions of ever moving stars accurately in relation to each other and define with any accuracy the edge of the Universe in every direction.

Len had also written:

Until Scientists can provide comprehensive answers to these fundamental questions, in particular the location of the centre of the Universe in relation to the Earth, then I believe we have to take on trust the theories, predictions and calculations made with regard to the age of the Universe, the enormous distances between the very old and new galaxies and the overall size of the Universe and significantly if and how it is expanding. For me, this information is essential to any claim made relating to the age of the Universe, the distance between stars and galaxies and the distance to the edge of the Universe.

If Stephen Hawking and other like-minded Scientists are correct and the Universe is still expanding then the mass that makes up the Universe, the billions of stars will be moving in an outward direction towards the edge of (something outside of the expanding Universe itself) away from the centre where the big bang occurred. The theories on an expanding Universe are based on the relationship of the stars as observed from Earth, the Hubble telescope and of course the ever-present computer models with their ability to undertake the mapping of the Universe and also simulate the big bang in film format, on a paper map or a flat monitor as fact. The danger being that 2-dimensional illustrations are used to describe and define 3-dimensional space, where everything however improbable can be shown to be possible. A classic example being a 'black hole' illustrated generally in 2-dimensional space looks perfectly feasible they always resemble whirlpools.

In reality if a black hole were to exist I believe it would be a sphere-shaped singularity condensing in size from all surfaces within the Universe,' defining the boundary of an imploding sphere-shaped object and portraying it in three rather than two dimensions other than computer programs would be rather difficult, even with the computer-generated model in 3-dimensional the black hole is mainly viewed in 2-dimensional format, on a TV or computer screen, to me, this observation is lost on many scientists. In the same way the scientist if he is to be persuaded in the existence of God, would want to know and see the location of heaven, where God resides, how old was he, black or white, male or female and if possible his passport photo and material proof that God exists. But physical proofs to those that doubt God's presence will never be enough and the proofs that do exist will always appear hollow to them.

Returning to the questions Len initially raised, I copied his notes onto my laptop.

If we study the stars in the Universe, they should be moving in tandem with each other on an outward path generally moving away from Earth. It is these stars Scientists use to predict the age and size of the Universe and that it's still expanding.

I read on:

We must consider that observing stars and the Universe from different parts of Earths hemisphere, for instance, say 'Australia or Newfoundland could be observed moving in different outward directions, some stars having the appearance of being either stationary or moving towards us. It could be that stars in either hemisphere are moving at different speeds and directions, some towards and some away from each other and earth.

What Len considered important and the point he wanted to make, was the relationship and distance between the stars, Earth and to each other can never fit one prediction or single formula. On a scrap of paper he had written:

Billions of stars some very old, 11 to 13 billion years old, whilst others relatively new 4 to 5 billion years old filling the night sky are moving either towards us, away from us or around us and each other, simultaneously in a vast Universe which it is claimed is still expanding, some now say too fast? Where does the Earth and our Solar system fit in? It is suggested that our tiny solar system formed some 5 billion years after the big bang, was formed from the emissions of dust and debris from a dying star. Current thinking suggests that the Universe is made up mainly of Dark Matter, Dark energy, with small amounts of Hydrogen, Helium, Neutrinos and heavy metals and that a dust cloud swirled around itself until it formed a huge mass, creating our sun and exploded again, following the same process forming the Earth and the other planets in our solar system; mainly from the residues of Helium and Hydrogen thrust from the Sun into millions of miles of empty space, forming the Earth, forever locked in its orbit around the Sun, its life force and creator.

Research shows that the Sun is made up mainly of hydrogen and helium with small amounts of carbon, neon, nitrogen and oxygen, whilst the earth is made up mainly of iron, silicon, magnesium, sulphur, nickel calcium, aluminium and oxygen with trace elements of gold, silver phosphorus, argon and all the other 118 elements identified in the 'Periodic Table' and of course the earths gravity which allows mankind to inhabit the earth and sustain life as we know it. To my knowledge, there are no signs that there is anywhere in the Universe that is remotely habitable. For me, these theories of the Earths creation as a living planet through natural evolution, with all the life form material in place is far too neat for me, unless of course, you accept God had a hand in the Earth's creation.

Five

Giza, Egypt November 2011

I can remember the day Len said to me.

"Henry, I can't tell you why, but I just don't believe the Earth simply unfolded as part of natural evolution.

I began to realise how agitated Len had become when he said. *"Is this really how life on Earth and mankind was created?"*

Now, in his father's apartment, there were papers everywhere, I found some more notes in his briefcase, it was like trying to complete a jig-saw where some of the pieces had been removed from the table, perhaps that was the challenge for me, trying to make sense of it all, I took Len's notes from the briefcase.

Today mankind has the tools to create life forms itself. The world we have fashioned is superior to Charles Darwin's world of natural evolution where the rest of life in all its forms resides mainly unchanged, oblivious of man's need for an explanation of everything. How does natural evolution correlate with the ever-expanding and unique mind of mankind?

There is the suggestion that Universe is contained within another Universe much like being part of a Galaxy rotating on its axes as it silently orbits a bigger and more profound object, much like the Earth orbits the Sun. This theory I found much more to my liking, it still didn't answer how the Universe was created but it might be a clue to how the galaxy we live in was formed. Part of the proof the big bang theory relates to radiation. In 1933 a radio astronomer Karl Jansky was credited with discovering cosmic microwave radiation. They identified the interference as static 'the distant echo' that followed the big bang. Most scientists go along with this theory but equally 'the distant echo' could be attributed to the creation of, a new galaxy, resulting from the explosion of a massive singularity, into the existing Universe.

Less likely was that an object nearly collided with the earth as depicted by Immanuel Velikovsky in his controversial book 'Worlds in collision' or the huge explosion created by the asteroid which some say collided with Earth some 65million years ago. Any of these events might have contributed to background radiation and if true might be the result of the distant echo, either partially or wholly. The trouble is we are dealing with events in the very distant past, trillions of miles from Earth. My aim is to get people to think and challenge these theories. Science is not always absolute, there are few truths but many possibilities, some that can never be proved, in addition Scientists, however brilliant, are also human, and fallible and prejudiced like the rest of us. The reality is that we come back to trying to assess what may have happened some thirteen billion years ago some trillions of miles distant, can we really be sure? As I have suggested, if this was the case it would answer the claim that God created the whole Universe.

Trying to unravel the questions posed by the Universes as just being, is like trying to juggle six balls in the air, while cycling round and round on a one-wheeled bike, ten feet off the ground, as a child I had watched a clown perform this act, thinking about it now, perhaps he was God in disguise, reminding us he was still here, watching us watching him. There would be a comfort zone if we viewed the Universe with a known centre, but without a known centre we are left with a complex puzzle with the cosmologist trying to plot the exact direction and speed of the billions of stars in space some billions of years old. It's worth noting that every picture of the Universe, which is 3-dimensional is pictured 2-dimensional and have no depth other than as imagined when we look up into the sky. Perception is what makes us want to discover the content of the Universe.

It was a fine balancing act, setting out Len's thoughts and ideas without being too influenced by what the scientific community were claiming and publishing. Most of the time Len was oblivious to outside influences, he had written:

I felt it was important that my thesis takes account of other claims and how difficult it is to make accurate observations about how we view the universe. We looked at the illustrations in Steven Hawking's book, The Universe in a Nutshell. To show how light bends Steven Hawking's had provided an illustration of a pear-shaped cone.

Len had made a copy of Stephen Hawking's drawing of the cone and had written:

The observer (we presume Earth-based) is shown viewing the Universe from the outer edge of the cone, i.e. the observer is looking at the Earth within the Universe as it was 5 billion years ago in the same timeframe as now, when the observer looks through a cone to view a flat-shaped Universe again the observer is outside of what he is viewing. Other than being conceptually wrong, I suggest the diagram also illustrates, just how difficult it is to view ever moving objects from within, in this case, from outside and within the Universe at the same time.

Len had also written:

There was another odd point to Stephen Hawking's illustration. The bottom of the pear-shaped object depicted the big bang, from where it is said the Universe was created. All the energy and light shown in the diagram is shown emitting in one conical upward direction towards the top of the cone where the observer is standing.

Len noted:

Had there been a big bang, the explosion would have showered matter in every direction not just in one direction, reflected light from the heat generated would also be travelling in every direction. The observation I make from Steven Hawking's illustration is that the observer, located at the edge of the cone looks down on to the Universe as he measures both the phenomena of bending light and the measurement of time both outside of the Universe and also within, 5,000 years ago, the same time. What concerned me was that the observer cannot be in two places at once in the same time frame.

The question of bending light was left unanswered by Len but the research led Len to the conclusion that unless the Earth were at the very centre of the Universe, which we know cannot be true as it was said to be formed only 4.5 billion years ago and is not the centre of anything, as we are part of the sun's solar system within the Milky Way, we might be much closer to one edge of the Universe than we realise. It would give substance to the claims that most stars, identified by red shift appear to be moving away from the Earth.

Len summed up his thoughts succinctly.

Unless we can find a way to travel faster than the speed of light Henry, Scientists will never be able to resolve these fundamental questions in any meaningful manner. Even with computers, I can't see how the edge of the Universe can be plotted with any degree of certainty. The Scientific claim that the Universe is still expanding, faster slower or not at all, will remain forever, no more than computer-based theory.

Of course, establishing the edge of the Universe has an appeal that lodges in every enquiring mind. Somewhere wonderful that we must find, a vision similar but much more dramatic than when we stand on the beach or a headland looking out towards the horizon where the sea meets the sky. Mankind's fascination and need for adventure, as explorers in search of Atlantis, an Eldorado or the Holy Grail, the beginning of time, finding a new life-supporting planet, traversing through space to the edge of the Universe, mankind's final frontier. Searching becomes addictive, an endless quest for those that believe discovery is mankind's destiny, who couldn't believe that finding the edge of the Universe was impossible, not me, I'm so excited.

Six

My take was a little different from Len's, why was mankind so pre-occupied with history with numbers and hard facts? Our history passed from one generation to the next, must be respected but the path that leads to an individual's fulfilment as we pass through time I believe is forward, not dwelling in the past, counting the number of stars in the Universe which ironically is changing every moment is a step backwards. For me, the future is not looking back, a point made by Castaneda's legendary Don Juan, no amount of history can take you forward, each generation, every one of us stands alone to interpret the past, the here and now and the future before them.

Len spent most of his time thinking, making notes or sitting in his armchair reading, he rarely went out. I had always been a bit of a film buff and having seen both 'Star Wars' and 'Star Trek' came to the conclusion that most Scientists who believe in space travel may also have seen these films which simulate space travel in a way that is not only spectacular but also entertaining, suggesting voyages to outer space are entirely feasible. In this scenario, it is easy for Scientists and Cosmologists to intentionally or unintentionally weave the fiction of these films into the fabric of what they research coming up with a 'faction' that puts meat on the bone of space travel in the pursuit of finding other life forms in the Universe. The opportunity of observing close up dark matter, dark energy, black holes, red and white dwarves and most importantly finding a new life-supporting planet that mankind can colonise.

The end result is a coming together of science and science fiction in a spectacular fashion, resulting in a new science, 'faction' being part fact and part fiction which pushes the barriers of reality and plausibility to the limit.

Over time this ever-growing mishmash of facts and fiction become so entwined that Scientists have to question if what they read and see is, a break though in scientific discovery or simply a theory modelled by the computer, the desire, the need to know and move forward can obscure fact from fiction. Something we both thought odd, was that the essential elements needed to create and sustain life on Earth, had seemingly found themselves on our tiny planet, having survived the huge temperatures they would have been subjected too during the formation of the planet, how could all the elements needed with all their complexity have randomly found themselves located in abundance on Earth, a tiny planet orbiting the Sun in the galaxy we call the Milky Way said to be some trillions of miles in size. It's hard to believe that we are alone in the Universe, in scientific terms it is difficult to accept that we occupy the Universe alone, could this really be possible? However, if God created the Universe and all that is within, mankind's occupancy of the Earth within the Universe becomes more plausible as do the numerous elements required to sustain life on Earth. Len said.

'Many Scientists believe in the theories around quantum mechanics, however pushing the frontiers of what is credible with more and more theories about the Universe seemed to have ignored Albert Einstein's theory of relativity. They explain to us as if they had witnessed the event for themselves in dramatic language, that huge amounts of matter are being swallowed up by black holes in space that 'alas we can't and never will see them'. But, the saving grace according to some Scientists, is that these unseen objects can be detected by small amounts of radiation emitted at the surface edge of

the black hole trillions of miles away and that dark matter populates the Universe and might tear itself apart as it continues to expand."

It was very easy to see how much this mattered to Len, in red capital letters he had written:

I DON'T KNOW WHO THESE PEOPLE ARE BUT THEY ARE NOT SCIENTISTS!!!

Calming down he added:

For ordinary people it is difficult to understand the science and maths that predict the size of the Universe, or that it is populated with billions if not trillions of stars, red and white dwarves and singularities and is around 13.7 billion years old and when spent following the big crunch will itself become a Singularity. It's not surprising that these scientific theories milling around exclude God and his handiwork.

During our research Len sensed that the dismissal of a God-created Universe by many in the science-based community might be based on fear, he wrote:

If God had existed and had played a part in the development of the Universe and mankind, then most of the established science relating to the origin of the Universe and in particular the evolution of mankind from the Chimpanzee would become redundant overnight. Fuelled by fears that Science would no longer lead the way in rational thinking, historic facts and much of the Science would become worthless. The biggest challenge to Science being, that another form of knowledge and power exists, which can never be evaluated and qualified in the way 'matter' can be quantified and would replace science as the pinnacle of man's understanding, faith, the belief in the here-after replacing hard facts and logic. The analysis being that there is life after death, when the soul leaves our body at the moment of death, with Scientists unable to quantify the unknown and God's power. Moribund, finding themselves in a lesser place, where science's value is never more than the sum of its material parts. For the

Scientist an even worse thought presents itself, the High Priests of religion with all their proclamations of life after death, heaven and hell, the mumbo jumbo of a supreme being would be back in vogue, reclaiming the high ground of the debate of when, where and how mankind originated.

Len's research led him to understand that, the measuring red shift of light, using Spectroscopy identifies stars and galaxies which are moving away from us and the blue shift identifies stars that are seemingly moving towards us. What puzzled Len was that if the Spectroscope science was so comprehensive, Scientists should be able to establish the centre of the Universe by tracking the stars' lines back to a central crossing point. But the lines of movement measured from stars trillions of miles from earth and said to be billions of years old must be minute and barely discernable. Stars viewed from Earth and then plotted (in 2-dimensional space, usually on a computer screen) identified as moving away from Earth could be moving in any outward direction, from approximately 129,600 specific points of direction from the original sphere-like object at the centre of the Universe that created the big bang.

Plotting and accurately recording the movement of stars of different ages trillions of miles away from Earth, moving in different directions to another in 3-dimensional space is much more complex and relies mainly on computer programs and modelling even if we ignore the fact that stars will be appearing and disappearing behind one another and the earth itself is continually moving towards or away from them in a different direction. For Len this was the nub of the problem, he had written this time in a more measured way:

Too many un-provable claims surround the creation of the

Universe, its size and complexity is theoretical. The research to hand whilst claiming to be able to map some 18,000 galaxies and identify a super structure named as 'the great wall' said to be some 600 million light-years in length and 250 million light-years in width is based on the same science that is unable to identify the centre of the Universe, which I have suggested is the key to confirming the age, size and formation of the Universe and if it is still expanding.

Len was keen to clarify his own, position. He didn't dispute that there are a huge number of galaxies and stars in the Universe. His concern was that much of the information on the colossal numbers quoted relating to size, age and movement is mainly computer-generated. He had already shown that assessing the actual number of stars in the Universe in a plausible manner or for the math to be properly checked is not viable in the time any one person has at their disposal, I quote Len's words.

One lifetime devoted to this task is not nearly enough, it would be daunting for an army of men to tackle the task. The problem is trying to assess how much of the science is properly established against the claims and information that might be wrong, where the theory cannot be proven in the same way that other scientific theories can be physically proved.

"Put another way," Len said

"Once Juan Sebastian Elcano had successfully navigated around the world in 1522 returning to his original point of departure, confirming Aristotle's belief in 330 BC that the Earth was spherical in shape and not a 2-dimensional flat surface. Though interestingly our perception when looking out to sea is that the horizon always appears as a flat level line and this will always be so when viewed from where we stand, no wonder that people were convinced that the Earth was flat."

I had to smile ruefully when as part of his research he

recalled.

"The Flat Earth Society' existed as late as 1960 having it is said some 3,000 members. Some of its publications in the 1970s and 80s stated, Galileo was a liar, Science Insults Your Intelligence, The World IS flat and that's that, and finally, Whole world deceived, except the very elite."

I had to laugh, in capital letters Len had written:

The FLAT EARTH BELIEVERS go about their LIVES unbeknown to them they WON'T FALL OF THE EDGE OF THE EARTH any time soon. Even when manned space travel had confirmed the distance from the Earth to the Moon sending back pictures taken from space, clearly showing the Earth as a sphere, you would think flattening once and for all the flat earth society member's beliefs but we would be wrong. There are still members in the Society who believe the Moon landings and space voyages were a 'hoax' filmed in a Hollywood Studio. Len referred to the 'flat earth believers' as the King Canute's of the Universe.

A nice take on the subject is made by Alan Lightman in his short essay 'Is the world round or flat? Len came bouncing into the living room one morning saying

"I've found it Henry." For once I had been up before him, his happy mood was a welcome change, I was always worried about the amount of time he spent working on the thesis. 'Found what Len?"

"I've found a scientist Henry, who actually writes in a way ordinary people can relate too, he describes things in such a simple easy manner, have you read any of Alan Lightman's books?"

Shaking my head I said, "No Len, I haven't."

"Well, he's written several books and essays on various subjects including, the 'Big Bang' and also Darwin."

He put the book he was holding 'Dance for two' down

on the coffee table. I picked it up and read the introduction. Len was right; the writing had a nice feel. Two days later I handed the book back to Len.

"Great book Len, I loved the essays about the Earth being round or flat', the visit of Mr Newton and his take on Steven Hawking's, Origin of the Universe, I agree Alan Lightman writes in a wonderful way, even I can understand, we need to research him more, find out what else he has written."

Seven

Giza, December 2011

It was midnight and I was ready for bed, it had been a long day. Not long enough for Len though, he walked over to the computer, switched it on, pulling the chair forward he made himself comfortable.

"I'll catch you in the morning," I said, Len half nodded without looking up, already he was engrossed in Alan Lightman's web site, he had that look of fused concentration on his face, I smiled and said 'good night' as I closed the door. The next morning Len suggested I make some notes, listing where he thought the science can be proved to illustrate his concerns over unproved science which he said relied mainly on theory, pad in hand I made the following notes.

"An example of good science being Andre Celsius, who established when water a liquid, changes to ice, a solid and also to steam, a vapour at a predictable temperature, this type of proof makes a huge difference to our perception and acceptance of phenomena i.e. when a substance changes its state before our eyes. Another simple but very good and important mathematical proof is Pythagoras Theorem, one of the foundations of geometry, whose basic principles 3 squared plus 4 squared equals 5 squared giving a 90-degree angle, which can easily be drawn on a piece of paper or on the ground and the squares of each side proved.

From geometry, sacred geometry was developed to create symmetry and divine proportion, the relationship and harmony between numbers, colour, form and sound, were an integral part of the design of the Great Pyramid of Giza and many other buildings of the early Egyptian Civilisation.

Len was all for making the point, that there were thousands of scientific theories which had been fully proved. He had already mentioned that scientists like to deal in 'absolutes'. His words below describe his thoughts.

"When proven the absolute becomes a known fact. As for example the square of 3 + the square of 4, equals the square of 5 (as found in Pythagoras theorem), easy enough, however belief in say life after death, faith healing, telepathy as examples, have many interpretations to their being and could be viewed in various ways. They are not and <u>never</u> can be absolutes, in the way scientists understand."

Len added.:

"There's no wrong way to believe Henry, but attempting to define belief, particularly in scientific terms is to demean it."

I agreed, recalling Don Juan, the Native American Sharman whom Carlos Castaneda met and described so vividly in a series of books, the first being, The Teachings of Don Juan. One day, by chance I met someone who claimed he was Don Juan shortly after I came to Giza; it was just before I met Len. I was sitting outside a café enjoying a coffee, people watching. A man dressed no differently from any other tourist visiting Egypt walked up to me, introducing himself as Don Juan. Sitting down unasked, he said he knew who I was and that he had read my thesis, adding that he was intrigued and had wanted to meet me. I looked at him, he could have been any age one moment he looked young, my father's age and then the next moment he looked very old and wizen. He had a playful grin on his face. Laughing he asked what was a North American Indian doing in Egypt? I was stunned but had no reason to disbelief the man wasn't Don Juan.

When I explained that I had come to Egypt to study Egyptology, he gave me a bemused look saying there was nothing to find here in Egypt that wasn't in America. Whilst I was shocked by the encounter, meeting someone who many people considered was no more than a fictional character of Carlos Castaneda's book, made me want to listen to what this man was saying, the coffee remained in the cup to go cold whilst I listened mesmerised. Whoever he was, he spoke of the 'implausible' in a way that stopped me dead in my tracks. He didn't attempt to explain what he meant but said in a crisp manner without a trace of emotion.

"No one can define belief, Mr Red Feather."

"It was," he said, "for each individual to constantly assess their own judgements."

Adding with a stony face which broadened into a wide grin and wagging a mischievous finger in the air.

"To understand anything Henry Red Feather, first you have to find then follow a path that has heart, it's all you need. If you follow the path that has heart, then the knowledge you seek will find you."

With that, he got up from his seat, donned his homburg hat bowed slowly and walked off disappearing into the crowd. I never met him again; it was the strangest thing that had ever happened to me in a long time.

"No one can define belief, Mr Red Feather."

His words rang in my ears for days. Had I really met Don Juan? Or was it some kind of apparition, a dream or a practical joke, was I losing my mind. I preferred to believe the meeting had actually happened, if it wasn't him, who was it and why would anyone else bother? Perhaps like Len, I was a little mad. Writing up these notes after Len's death, alone in his apartment I recalled Don Juan's words, wondering what they would have made of each other had they met. I think if Len had gotten over the initial shock of Don Juan's humour, tricks and riddles he would have liked and respected him. I felt sure he would have asked him what books he had read. Equally, Don Juan would have laughed out loud saying, there was no time to waste counting stars and reading books. Life was too short and time far too important to waste stargazing and reading books, saying, "I have better uses for sheets of paper."

If Len was listening, I think he might have laughed as well; Don Juan's humour was so infectious. I think Don Juan would have recognised immediately that Len was different from most people he had met. He would have seen beyond Len's frail stature, his weak facial features and shyness, finding a young man of enormous intellect and sureness of thought. I was certain that Don Juan would have listened to Len with understanding, recognising that they were on different paths, both in search of knowledge. Their paths leading to the same place, understanding! But approached from entirely different directions. Although Len had never met Don Juan or read any of Castaneda's books, he had at the time listened intently to my account, of Don Juan and Carlos Castaneda the brilliant author of the four initial books which made up 'The teachings of Don Juan. When I had finished, he nodded in agreement saying:

"The danger for the scientific community Henry is its ability to believe in its own invincibility, as if calculations and theories establish facts that can't be wrong."

I listened fascinated as Len went on to say:

"Many current scientific theories are so complex they require vast machines and computers to support the claims made, it is not possible for the layman to be able to challenge the Scientist and their science. If it's physical proof you want, on say the prospect of finding life on Andromeda first you would you need to plan a journey which could take 1100 generations to reach. You would need to wrap up and keep warm, the temperature is said to be minus 275.6 degrees Celsius, just 2.5 degrees above absolute zero a cold, unmoving desolate place."

There was a trace of sarcasm in Len's voice. I thought of my father Bald Eagle back at the homestead in Arizona, wondering what he would have made of Len. Remembering as a child how we would sit at night around the camp fire, looking up into the night sky, he would pick out various stars and tell me stories of his adventures when he was a boy, folk legends, the Indian way of understanding the Universe, the names his forefathers gave to the stars. Returning to the present, I found myself saying,

"So the Scientist would never be able to reach Andromeda in his life time."

Len looked at me benevolently,

"No Henry, he wouldn't."

I nodded slowly saying, "Not even if he was travelling at the speed of light?"

He waved me one of his forbearing looks, *"The answer's still no!"*

Eight

Giza December 21st 2011

We were having breakfast on the patio; it was going to be a glorious winter day, not too hot but warm enough for tee shirt and jeans. Len got up and walked over to the balustrade, he turned back and said.

"I met a young Astronomer when I was at Oxford, he was so full of himself and his theories regarding stars and galaxies he made me feel sick. Do you want to hear the story, Henry?"

"Go on then," I said, wondering what was coming next.

"Well, when I was in my final year at Oxford there was this chap, Algernon Butterfield, a fellow student two years older than myself. He was always banging on about the expanding Universe and how quantum mechanics would enable people to travel through Space. He likened himself to Galileo. 'A pioneer of quantum astronomy' was how he described himself. He would make anyone he could find, sit and listen to his theories in his rooms, where he held court. I got roped in a couple of times.

I have to say, Butterfield was a crushing bore. On one occasion when he had finished his monologue on time travel, he challenged anyone to come up with a better theory. I think you know me well by now Henry."

He looked at me and smiled.

"I'm usually too retiring, wouldn't say boo to a goose, but I was so angry with his blasted rhetoric I raised my hand."

I nodded, "What happened Len?"

"Butterfield was initially surprised then he said; Okay King Farouk if you've got something to say spit it out. I had decided enough was enough and asked him if he had seen or knew anything about John Constable's famous painting, The Hay Wain. Butterfield looked at me with contempt, 'Have you been listening to a word I have been saying Farouk? I have Butterfield, if you give me five minutes, I have an alternative suggestion as to how we measure time and perceive events of the past.

And you know something I don't Farouk? Butterfield began laughing as he looked around at the assembled students, a command in his withering smile. Silence everyone, King Farouk is about to enlighten us."

Len looked at me half smiling, saying that at the time he had been petrified and wished he hadn't opened his big mouth.

"Here's the story anyway," he said with a smile.

"Butterfield I said, Cosmologists like yourself spend a lot of time looking and analysing stars, attempting to define their age and position relative to the Earth and each other, whilst the artist with his paints and brushes captures just one moment it time. John Constable's, Hay Wain is an example. It's a landscape painting depicting a hay wain in the middle of a millpond, there are two horses, two men and a woman close by her cottage, there is a fisherman and a dog, the picture captures a typical summers day in the country, immortalising the landscape it depicts. I could see Butterfield was getting agitated and about to say something but I raised my hand waving him down saying, Butterfield, I listened to you without interruption, please afford me the same courtesy. As you would expect, he gave me a filthy look, telling me gruffly, get on with it then. I refused to be drawn and calmly said.

The picture was painted by Constable in 1821 which after an indifferent reception became a very famous painting. It has been photographed and printed in poster and book form thousand upon thousands of times; Copies of the painting are available in nearly every country of the world. The painting depicts a scene, nearly two hundred years ago, the people in the picture along with the horse and dog,(if they were real and actually lived as opposed to be a figment of the artist's imagination), have died, the hay and wagon no doubt have rotted or decomposed. The fleeting clouds have long passed to be replaced by more clouds over the years and the landscape has changed, worn by wind and rain warmed and stimulated by the Over the last two hundred years the picture hanging in the National Gallery, has travelled some twenty-five thousand miles every day as the Earth orbits the Sun 365 days each year for the last 180 years a total distance around 1,644,750,000 miles.

The painting unmoved still in its frame, hanging on the wall has survived mainly intact, there will have been some loss of colour, the quality of the canvas and picture frame will have become fragile but for the observer today the painting looks much like when it was first painted but the people, the dog and the horse depicted in the painting, live on in the painting, frozen in one moment of time, coming alive in the minds and imaginations of the observer. There are thousands of prints and photographs of the painting all over the world. Countless articles have been written about every aspect of the painting, one could say that the people and animals captured in the painting are immortal.

I must stop you there Farouk, Butterfield had shouted. This cooked up story has nothing to do with astronomy; he looked around the room, seeking support for his outburst. There was a deathly silence in the room, no one knew what to say, then he screeched, nothing, nothing, nothing, it has nothing to do with astronomy Farouk."

I could tell Len was enjoying recounting his clash with Butterfield, he was trying not to laugh, it was one of the few times in the months since we had met that he looked at ease and truly relaxed.

"What happened Len?"

"I stood my ground Henry," I said, "you're right Butterfield, the painting has nothing to do with astronomy but it has everything to do with how we perceive time, space, events and the value judgements we make. If a painting has a value greater than the sum of its 2-dimensional representation on canvas, it shows us another way to see and perceive a moment in time, in a way that science and mathematics never can.

In your world Butterfield, the stars in the Universe, billions of years old appear to have hardly moved over a period of around 5,000 years or ever since mankind has been observing and plotting their position in the Universe, this is an illusion. If we accept that some stars are 10 billion years old the movement of the star moving either towards or away from Earth could be expressed as follows: The presumed age of the oldest stars 10,000,000,000 years, divided by the time spent observing them = 5,000 years. From its original position in the Universe the movement of a star could be said to be 0.0000005 from the original plotted position. That is the 5,000 years mankind has been plotting the position of the stars. This is why stars always appear stationary in the sky, observing a star for 5,000 years which is 10 billion years old is nothing more than a blink of the eye. A star's apparent permanence, as viewed from Earth is an illusion. In a different way, Constables painting is also an illusion. Freezing time into one moment and then as the years and centuries come and go, the one moment captured in the painting remains the same as it was when first painted, passing through time. Time, matter and space intrigue the Scientist so much that his enquiry and subsequent research must be provided with answers, it is a scientists nature to insist on having answers, perhaps in different ways, we all do, but not to the same intense degree.

People like you Butterfield, are driven by an endless desire and a need to quantify and explain everything, first the Earth and every living object, then the Sun and the solar system and finally the Universe the final frontier of your research. A Scientists every breath, each moment is focused on a relentless journey of discovery developing new theories and answers to the endless questions that require measurement, quantified by calculations. Butterfield started to speak again, putting his hand up like a child in a primary school class, but I waved him down again.

Let me explain Butterfield, art in all its forms re-creates life in its own image running parallel with reality. In Constables famous painting the people and animals have become immortal. Critics of art, using the principals of science and logic have tried to evaluate aesthetic expression but there are no measurements or calculations for art. Constables painting creates immortality on a piece of canvas. It could equally have been a novel, a page in a book, a music score, a love letter or the lyrics of a song, great writers, composers, musicians, poets, actors and ballet dancers, all have the ability to transport us through time and space in a way that science and mathematics never can.

Once in a while an artist, musician or a writer touches everyone with their greatness, leaving behind in their work a legacy that speaks universally to each of us, retaining its freshness and appeal from one generation to the next. Great art is timeless. On another level there is a need for people as individuals and collectively to leave a legacy at the time of their death, a need to be remembered, it's the nature of humans to seek immortality on Earth as well as planning for life after death. In reality, for most of us, our Earthly legacy will be no more than a faded photograph of us when we were children, a copy of our birth, certificate, graduation, weddings and holiday snaps. The final record, the death certificate, our names etched on a gravestone with a date and the words 'RIP' or 'in loving memory'. For the Actor the starring role in a movie, 'Gone with the wind', 'Casablanca' or 'The Godfather' provide celluloid immortality, for the supporting cast and extras a walk-on part, their names forever captured in the rushes. For the writer, artist, scientist, explorer and sportsman perhaps a Nobel Peace Prize, a gold medal, a name in the record books, a biography or an obituary in the broadsheets. For Khufu immortality came in the form of the magnificent 'Pyramid of Giza' the first and only remaining wonder of the ancient world. For the Astor anoraks Butterfield, such as you, immortality might be having a star named after him. I paused for a moment; I wish I could describe to you the look on Butterfield's face when I said, I name this dead star 'The Butterfield red dwarf, discovered by Algernon Butterfield on April the first 2012. Everyone in the room burst out laughing, except Butterfield, some even started clapping; I carried on where I had left off, I hadn't finished with him. For Andy Warhol, his famous prints of Cam bells soup tins 1962, the prints of Marylyn Monroe and Chairman Mao' where art apes and replaces life with a printed piece of paper. Another example of immortality Butterfield, being Conan Doyle's famous detective Sherlock Holmes, admired worldwide for his ability to solve the most complex of crimes. Better known and more revered than real detectives, anyone reading of his adventures for the first time might be forgiven for expressing disappointment that Holmes and his companion Doctor Watson were no more than figments of Conan Doyle's imagination. Such is the potency of the characters now given celluloid flesh and blood, if you saw them on the television, could you be sure they weren't actually alive? If you are interested Butterfield, Holmes address is 225B Baker Street, London.

The time machine is more likely to be a book, a film, the theatre, a picture or photograph than a rocket-propelled space ship, the closest we are going to get to deep space travel is watching 'Star Trek' or latterly 'The National Geographic film Journey to the Edge of the Universe' surprisingly, the celluloid journey takes only an hour and a half to travel trillions of miles on film, such is the power of the computer and simulation or perhaps it tells us something of the timespan of man's ability to concentrate."

Len went on to say that Butterfield, his face growing redder by the minute had started hyper venting then shouting. *"I never heard such poppy cock in my life Farouk,"* turning to the other students for reassurance. Len was now laughing uncontrollably.

"No I don't expect you have Butterfield, it's nothing less than I would have expected from you."

I smiled saying,

"My father Bald Eagle would have liked the story Len; you must have some Indian blood in you as well as Egyptian."

September 2012

Now four months since Len's death, leafing through Len's papers I found a totally different take on how Len described time, the notes were dated 12th of January 2012.

Time is the creation of mankind or perhaps an alien intelligence. Okay, I note you might rightly say animals, birds, plants, flowers - all forms of life respond to the cycles of time on earth as it orbits the sun and in turn, the moon orbits the earth but other forms of life don't record time in the complex way we humans do. Neither is it necessary to make time into something tangible and solid. In the developed world we have the most precise clocks, watches and instruments to tell the time and a refined way of recording various activities associated with and measured by time. One might ask, does time exist in itself without there being anything to record or is time only a mathematical concept that exists only in mankind's mind?

We might consider whether time, is necessary and essential to our lives. However, time is one way of giving meaning and framework to our lives in the shape of rules to live by as well as an array of abstract thoughts. For many people living in the framework of time is essential to their wellbeing and without the framework of time they might fall apart. Dare I say we might be better off without the development of time in its current framework, where so many people feel their lives are governed by time? How unstable would we become, if there were no calendars or clocks, nothing to record, or to tell us the time of day or how long we have lived, the age of the earth, the stars and the Universe?

I hate to say it but I believe I would worry less and feel more secure within myself, if I could break free of the rigid framework of time that governs my life. I notice Henry's life doesn't revolve around time in the same way that mine does, he's a free spirit whilst I am trapped in space-time and numerology. Since the 20th century, scientists and physicists though not all suggest that objects such as huge stars can bend time and the fabric of space, this for me is really shaky ground, I don't believe it for a moment, forgive the pun. The latest take for those interested in the Universe's creation and development, resolves around String Theory, Superstring Theory and latterly multiple string theory, theories as complex, un-provable and perhaps as meaningless as science can get.

Henry bought me Brian Greene's book, The Elegant Universe, beautifully written, authoritative and goes a long way for making the case for a Universe formed around a series of strings. Like all great writers, Greene leaves room for alternatives theories, the principal one being Quantum Mechanics, other than the Universe being created by God, my preference leans towards Einstein. In purely scientific terms his theories are more appealing to me than Edward Written and Max Plank's theories based on string, superstring theory and quantum mechanics, apparently you can't have both theories, but when all said and done each one of us, whether a physicist, scientist, amateur astronomer or the man or woman on the street, we are alone with what we believe, when our short lives on earth come to an end and time as we know it, is no more. Our ideas, beliefs and theories, for some, a lifetime's work, condensed into a book, stand silently waiting to be read and take their place in the afterlife of immortality.

I once heard someone say, this chap was ahead of his time, but unless there is life after death, time whether bent or otherwise, is of no relevance to me.

It was 6 months before his death that Len told me his story about Butterfield, one minute he was up and happy then I watched the laboured way he returned to his computer and his sudden change of mood. Now 5 months after his death I put down his notes on time and leafed through Brian Greene's book still in the apartment. There was a passage I wanted to review regarding space-time. Greene had written that physicists were stopped from fully understanding the relationship between the crunching of time, space and matter sighting the moment of the big bang as the cause. Len had concluded in his notes that nothing changes, scientists, physicists will never be able to describe the interaction between time, space and matter unless they can find out what was happening prior to the big bang. Len called the scientific dilemma. 'The elephant in the room'. *Noting in red, that God knew the answer but it wouldn't be the answer that scientist's wanted to hear.*

I remember as if it was yesterday, the moment I looked over at Len, oblivious to my presence. He was coming up twenty-six years of age but looked more like sixty, his face was a road map of deep lines etched into his skin, caused no doubt by thinking too hard. That day poor Len, he seemed lost, trapped in the framework of time, space and matter, though on a good day his enigmatic smile gave him a much younger look. He was right about my not being as intense about time as he was, but in the few months I had known Len, I was just an ordinary American Indian walking in his footsteps, in my mind, the footsteps of greatness.

My concern at the time was about Len's health and state of mind. For me Len was a brother, I had never met anyone remotely like him, brilliant but fragile, my job as I saw it was to look after him and protect him, mainly from himself. I used to tell myself, time and its blasted framework would have to wait; I had more important things on my mind. Looking back, it's hard to accept that I had failed Len, something I would have to live with but knowing Len was something I never wanted to forget.

65

Nine

Giza Christmas Eve 2011

Christmas Eve was low key, Len was reading, whilst I read through Len's brief notes on time, and thinking back to his clash with Butterfield, I realised that he had only in part enjoyed recounting the story of, Butterfield and Constable's painting of 'The Hay Wain' later that evening in a more sombre mood he came over to me and said.

'It's never enough Henry, the Scientist has to continue his research, to find and dissect truth until there is nothing left to dissect in the search of the absolute."

He was, of course, describing himself, apart from being a brilliant mathematician and a perfectionist, Len was pragmatic. It was his idea, that a simple way of separating hard and soft scientific facts from each other needed to be developed, to ensure he said that 'scientific wishful thinking' was removed from the journals and that un-provable theories brought into the public domain were properly qualified. The object he said was to protect the good science.

We were having dinner in his flat, the dining area overlooked the Great Pyramid in the distance, there was a glorious pink hue filling the sky in the fading sunset. I knew something was on Len's mind just the way he put his knife and fork down. I waited, smiling, there was a look of amusement on his face as he exclaimed.

"Do you know Henry that at the age of 16, Einstein wrote that 'Invention is not the product of Logical thought even though the final

product is tied to a logical structure?"

I replied that I didn't, although I was hungry I realised there was more to come so I put my knife and fork down. Len's line of thought was usually beyond me but there was intensity when he spoke that evening that made me want to listen, he was burning up, bursting with energy ready, ready to relate his latest thoughts, it was if I had a shotgun and he was under starter's orders.

"Come on then Len, let's have it."

"Henry, there's so much mumbo jumbo out there, stuff wrapped around scientific mythology: someone on the web stated that using a balloon he had been able to confirm that the 'Universe was Flat', that's it, the Universe is flat no more research required, end of story, a new fact."

I asked Len why this statement upset him so much, could it be true, that the Universe is flat.

"You're right to ask Henry, it might be flat but how flat is flat, the Sun has a diameter of 864,340 miles and the distance between the Earth and the Sun is between 91 and 94 million miles which suggests the Universe is not exactly flat."

When we got into this type of discussion Len was always patient with me, he smiled then looked across the balcony towards the outline of the enigmatic Sphinx which we could just make out from the balcony. The Sphinx had that timeless gaze, staring out into space, like Constable's painting but in a much more dramatic way it had also defied time.

Len turned back to me; the smile had gone, his mood changing.

"Yes, the Universe could be described in scientific terms as flat but that's not the point Henry." He pushed his hands through

the air as he often did when he was becoming agitated, saying.

"What is needed, Henry, when Scientists speculate in this way is a clear form of qualification, a way to show that the theories and claims can be identified in terms of quality of proof, one way would be colour coding."

I sensed Len was now entering one of his brainstorming sessions, so leaving my own food half-finished, I picked up a pad and started making some notes.

*"We could start with colour coding Henry, Green where the science has been established by physical proof, Amber where the science is waiting for confirmation or is in dispute and Red where the theory hasn't and never can be physically proven. The big bang theory other than as simulated in film or from a computer model cannot be proved and never will, we cannot unravel time however hard we try, **Red**. The theory of a steady-state Universe whether it is open or flat, expanding or crunching, cannot be physically proved and never will unless we are able to travel faster than the speed of light, 186,000 miles per second and for the space traveller to live for several thousand years, travelling at 56,000km per hour would take approximately 81,000 years to reach the galaxy of Andromeda, **Red**."*

Len hardly stopped for breath as he continued to explain:

*"Henry it's unlikely that Black holes can be physically detected and established, we need to remember the distances we are dealing with, the nearest is trillions of miles away and according to the science, anything close simply disappears, I give this a **Red**.*

*Likewise, the number of stars in the Universe cannot be verified in any meaningful manner, who maps the billions of stars in a comprehensive manner, has anyone actually counted the 200 billion stars in the Milky Way and who audits the data? **Amber no Red**.*

*The prospect of dark matter, anti-matter and dark energy existing has no plausible meaning other than words that appear in science fiction and comics. They all sound exciting and mysterious when spoken but this type of jargon has no place in Science. Einstein's theory of relativity would be the first casualty of its existence, **Red**."*

He paused momentarily.

"It is not good enough for Cosmologists and Scientists to claim the Universe is expanding and that perhaps there is no explanation for its presence other than 'it is' there is no pre-history for the Big Bang or the Universe, this is not acceptable Red, Red, Red."

I put in my small contribution.

"The moon rotates around the Earth every 28 days as the Earth spins on its own axis passing through Greenwich meantime every 24 hours as it orbits the sun every 365.25 days, Green or Amber Len?"

Len looked through me as if he hadn't heard a word I had said, his mind racing onto the next area of discussion.

"Green Henry, but don't go funny on me, there are some bad scientific theories out there. Some Scientists suggest that once we are able to combine quantum mechanics with the use of worm holes, the fourth dimension and warp time, we will be able to travel faster than the speed of light popping up anywhere in space. These Scientists accept that we would need to ignore the theory of relativity to travel across the Universe in any meaningful way and I would suspect many other simple rules of science would also fall by the wayside."

I listened to Len, I had never seen him so animated, it was getting late but he was now in overdrive, I went to get another pad.

"Without proper clarification Henry, claims based on conjecture turn the good space research into a nightmare of flawed science that

brings into question the good and established science. It could be called fantasy science or more accurately anti science."

Len suddenly stopped talking, ate a morsel of food and then carried on talking.

"*My basic rule of science is you can't create something out of nothing or put another way, you can't replace something with nothing, this is the nub of the 'Big Bang' issue we face Henry.*"

I didn't have a clue what he was talking about but listened anyway.

"*When scientists tell us that the Universe is 13.7 billion years old populated by billions or even trillions of stars, their words have little or no real meaning or significance for ordinary people, because the numbers quoted can't be compared or measured against anything we actually know as fact, we the general public are left in limbo. The science sounds impressive and plausible and sometimes presented with qualifications, but its bad science.*"

There was a trace of a smile on Len's face.

"*I am glad you're making notes Henry.*"

I had faithfully recorded Len's thoughts and notes, I liked the idea of qualifying un-proved science but most of what he actually said was lost on me.

A while after Len's death I came across a book in the library, that would have interested him. It was the Faith of a Physicist by HE Huntley written in 1960. To my knowledge, there weren't that many books written by scientists that combined the wonders of science with the wonders of creationism.

It was a small volume and an easy read, Huntley's observation that 'the day of the layman without scientific training being able to follow the Physicists' progress in the atomic world is over'. Huntleys book took me by surprise, his take on physics and religion was strange, refreshing and compelling, there was little about Charles Darwin's theory of natural evolution, Alfred Wallace wasn't even mentioned, instead Huntley quoted lines from famous poets, such as Shakespeare and extracts from the Bible to illustrate his views as a scientist on his belief and support of creationism. Whether you agreed with his views was another matter, the absence of at least a paragraph on natural evolution I thought was a weakness in Huntleys theories. But, in any event the book had a certain charm and was wholly original; I suspect some academics would have condemned his work when it was first published as a betrayal and damaging to the integrity of Science. I got the feeling Huntley didn't care too much, he wanted his say and the book adequately expressed his thoughts. I think Huntleys book would have pleased and reassured Len, but since its publication in the nineteen sixties, the world of science has changed at an incredible pace. The books place in history is to depict science as a warmer place than the bleak cold scientific facts of life that always end with death as the final act. Huntley was one of a rare breed, a scientist who bowed to a greater science than that of the big bang and Darwin's theory of natural evolution, he bowed like all true Christians, to the science of creationism, for which there are no calculations, formulas or proof, just the simple belief that the world and our being is the work of God.

Ten

Giza 2nd of January 2012

I walked into the living room; Len was hunched over the computer, surrounded by pieces of paper, handwritten notes some on the desk others littering the floor around a stack of books piled up to his knees beside the swivel chair. Considering just how many pieces of paper there were lying around, I guessed he hadn't gone to bed. Over the past three or four weeks since we had begun our research, Len it seemed didn't want to sleep, whilst I desperately needed to sleep, but couldn't.

"Morning Len, I'm getting some coffee, do you want some?"

Half turning, he looked at me vacantly as if was I someone he had just met.

"No thanks Henry," he said putting the laptop to one side and gathering together some of his papers. I had the feeling Len was going to say something as I started to walk towards the kitchen, I didn't have long to wait.

"The danger for Scientists Henry is their believing every word they say, as if their words were facts in themselves."

His cheery voice told me he was in one of is expressive moods as he spoke between mouthfuls of toast, his tea was studiously ignored, I was still trying to wake up, it had been another long and sleepless night, I sensed this wasn't going to stop Len letting me know his latest thoughts.

"Henry, Charles Darwin spent much of his life formulating

theories about natural evolution, linking mankind's existence to that of the chimpanzee from which we are informed, humans first mutated around 5 million years ago. A big time difference from when it was recorded in the Bible, that God created Heaven and Earth, a few thousand years ago."

I picked up my note pad and a pencil and went over to the leather armchair and made myself comfortable; the coffee was hot and good, I was ready.

"Many of Charles Darwin's theories over the last hundred and fifty years have been proved right. Christopher Wills in his painstaking book 'The Runaway Brain' confirms that the process of DNA mutation (in evolutionary terms) is so slow and complex and the evidence linking mankind to the chimpanzee is irrefutable, maybe but I will never accept that natural evolution is the complete story of mankind. If there is a weakness in Darwin's theories regarding the descent of mankind? It might be found in a small group of people that we refer to as child prodigies, polymaths, autodidactics, the genius and savants, who between them have knowledge that is innate rather than acquired, sublime and unfathomable. How do this small group of people acquire their innate knowledge, I don't believe it was passed down by the Chimpanzee, Henry."

Len looked pleased with himself, I wondered where he was going with this; he noticed the puzzled look on my face, with a warm smile saying.

"Henry, anthropologists like Alfred Wallace and Charles Darwin spent their lives immersed in study. It's easy for people like them to become engrossed in their work and overlook or miss the obvious, information that could challenge or clarify the theories they are seeking to prove. For example, in terms of human natural evolution. Just look at the early Egyptian civilisation, where do they fit into Wallace or Darwin's theories of natural evolution?"

Len pursed his lips, sweeping his hand through his hair,

saying with a theatrical flourish.

"I don't think so!"

Len finished his toast and got up to begin his morning ritual of pacing the room in his slippers, the tatty dressing gown tied tightly around his waist, the Oxford university scarf worn like a cravat, I guessed he was cold, he was smiling but looked agitated and began pacing around the lounge, it was his way of clarifying his thoughts. Suddenly he stopped pacing, standing by the window he continued.

"Henry, the greatest civilisation known to mankind arose sometime around 7,000 years ago in the Nile delta. The Egyptian people were provided with a rich, fertile land a climate that was perfect providing an abundance of food and maintaining a stable and comfortable lifestyle. This doesn't explain in any way the emergence of a wonderful civilisation with its breathtaking monuments, magnificent architecture, hieroglyphics, spells, paintings and furniture. These artefacts remain sufficiently intact for us to glimpse into another world, infinitely more refined than our own. The Egyptians from around 5,000 BC to 500 BC left behind a timeless beauty that has captured the imagination of every succeeding generation of people from across the world. This on its own tells us something of their greatness and significance.

For some reason perhaps their indulgence in idolatry, hedonism or another series of events led to their downfall, the bible refers to the ten plagues that God inflicted on the Egyptian Empire, sadly for whatever reasons, the magnificence that was Egypt is no more. When you see how the Egyptians live today in the shadow of its past greatness, it's hard to comprehend just how talented their ancestors were, but the artefacts remain as proof of their greatness."

Len was standing by the window looking out to the desert and the pyramids silhouetted by the morning sun.

"The brilliance of the Egyptians can never be recaptured Henry,

like everyone else who has studied Egyptology, I often wonder, how did it come to end? Something very strange or dramatic must have happened."

"A considerable number of people have spent their lives trying to answer that question Len."

Len nodded in agreement, adding.

"HG Wells made a better case for establishing mankind as part of natural evolution than Darwin, there is much to underpin natural evolution in his book 'The outline of history', he writes that the first life on Earth came from sea then to land, followed by reptiles, flying dragons, the development of mammals before mankind arrived. To my mind, HG Wells was a better writer than Charles Darwin. He comes across as more worldly. Curiously though, Well's didn't attend church or believe in any formal religion but he wasn't an atheist either, I'm inclined to think, God resided in his head, in a way he behaved like a God, we can tell this from his books, 'God The Invisible King', 'A Modern Utopia', The War of The Worlds' and the 'Time Machine', to mention a few of his books. Herbert G Wells to give him his full name, Henry, is one of my heroes, he was a genius, Henry."

It was nice to see Len at ease with himself, so often he was either pensive or agitated; I smiled as he carried on revealing his thoughts.

"In any event Henry, the real question for Darwinists relating to 'the evolution of mankind' is why the Chimpanzee is still a Chimpanzee eating bananas' after millions of years? Why hasn't the Chimpanzee evolved in a similar way to humans, who have changed out of all recognition to their said ancestors? It's too neat Henry and far too simple for the anthropologists to claim that every life form, can be traced back along Darwinist lines of evolution, with the first forms of life evolving from the sea millions of years ago with man at the head of the chain of natural evolution."

Len suddenly stopped talking, sat down and took a swig of cold tea that made me pull a face.

"Urgh, Len how can you drink cold tea?"

Either he hadn't heard or didn't consider my question of any relevance.

"Henry, I don't dispute the Chimpanzee is man's first cousin but our forefather's? That can never be the whole story. Something dramatic must have happened other than Chimpanzees evolving into humans."

He looked at me with an apologetic smile.

"There's no easy way to say this Henry, but the Egyptian way of life, their magnificence and style shows the difference between the Chimpanzee, stone age man and other isolated human civilisations then or now. No! The Egyptian civilisation of 5,000 BC to 500 BC was too wondrous and civilized to be simply described as part of mankind's natural evolution."

He paused and went over to his notes picking up a piece of paper.

"Here it is."

He was becoming animated as he read from his notes.

"In the 1960s John Gurdon a scientist did something brilliant and unexpected Henry.

"What did he do Len?"

"He created a tadpole, Henry."

I arched my eyebrows in mock surprise, wondering what was coming next.

"By taking a single cell from the intestines of a mature frog removing its genes and placing it in a cell of a frog's egg. The result was a cloned frog. It was the beginning of cloning and what scientists

call stem cell technology. The tadpole was followed by a clowned animal, Dolly the Sheep in 1996. Today human cloning is within the grasp of Doctors. Who is to say that in the time before the Egyptian civilisation, God hadn't also experimented with different forms of being, as part of creationism?"

He looked at me in an odd way, I wasn't sure if I was meant to reply, I tried hard to think of something to say but before I could, he began talking again.

"A number of Egyptian murals and Hieroglyphs depict several Gods who played an active part in their lives, for example, there was Set (Seth) the God of storms, shown with the head of a jackal and a human body. Or Anubis the God of the dead, drawn with the head of a rodent or mongoose and a human body, then there is Seker the falcon God drawn with the head of a falcon with a human body."

I looked at the photograph of a papyrus depicting Seth, he handed me, it was mesmerising, I handed it back to Len.

"Henry, who were these Animal, headed people? And what about the Sphinx depicted with the head of a woman and the body of a lion, are we to accept that these curious forms just appeared in the minds of the Egyptian people as 'symbols of Gods' to be worshipped? I don't think so. I am more inclined to believe they are representations of actual beings, perhaps Demi God's, who ruled Atlantis and were destroyed in the great flood that removed Atlantis from the face of the earth around 8,000 to 10,000 BC. What I am saying Henry, is these animal-headed creatures didn't just appear in the imaginations of the Egyptians, they were too educated and intelligent, not given to fanciful thoughts, their recorded history tells us that."

I listened in awe, wondering what Len was going to say next.

"Humans have the power of abstract thought Henry; something which I believe has no place in natural evolution. An animal's

behaviour, its actions and reactions are concentrated on daily survival and the need to reproduce, though this is not to demean their intelligence, in many ways equal to the intelligence of humans but very different and used in a very different and limited way, they don't have the time or energy to waste on abstract thought."

Len began pacing around the room again.

'No, Abstract thought belongs to mankind alone. Refined, distilled into the sciences, mathematics, painting, literature and every other manmade abstract expression and has no place in natural evolution. I acknowledge humans and the chimpanzee might run parallel to each other as they evolved but they are unconnected, they are not our forefathers, who was it that said, life mimics art?"

Was he asking or telling me? It sounded a bit like Oscar Wilde or perhaps Andy Warhol, whoever it was the quotation sounded apt, to me it meant that Art came first, paving the way of how we might live and progress, not art following life, recording mankind's evolution, well that was my take on what Len was saying. I watched him pacing around the room as he spoke.

"Henry, our ability to indulge and more importantly to set down on paper, in film and computer our 'thoughts', is what sets humans apart from animals and other forms of life. I believe the essence of abstract thought, challenges Charles Darwin's theory of natural evolution at its core. A point made by the much younger anthropologist Alfred Wallace, who having initially agreed with Darwin, when both their papers on natural evolution were published in 1859. By 1889 Wallace had distanced himself from Darwin's stated position, saying in his memories that the development of the human brain, in mathematics, did not lend itself to natural evolution."

This was interesting, I had come to the same conclusion some time ago, listening to Len confirmed my own thoughts and made me smile, as I scribbled down my notes. I wished I had brought a tape recorder; Len seemed to understand, smiling as he waited for me to catch up.

"Henry, animals have no need for Albert Einstein to discover 'the theory of relativity' Dirac's theories of Quantum Mathematics or any other theory for that matter. Relativity is simply a theory, an interpretation of how the Universe works but like all 'theories' words and numbers are no more than records of what we observe, they are unnecessary to maintain life on Earth. Abstract thought resides outside the requirements of maintaining life. Theories are independent of real-life and its daily needs. Abstract thought, in art, mathematics, literature, poetry move through time, unconcerned and unaffected by cause and effects of the past or future, they just are and defy qualification."

I wondered what Professor McDonald would have made of Len's latest theories, I suspect he would have us both locked up and thrown the key away. It was wonderful to watch and listen to Len at ease with himself, I wondered how long these ideas had been piling up, ready to be released on an unsuspecting public, he smiled as he continued with his account of human evolution.

"The existence of 'abstract thought' Henry whether good or bad, whatever their meanings or value are from their inception independent of the people who created them once in the public domain, unchanging they are immortal. History records mankind's most significant thoughts and ideas in books, paintings, films and the like. By their presence and passing of time, new myths and legends are created, a mirror of real life. Some great ideas and theories have a huge bearing on how each generation, interpret their own existence and provide answers to the age-old questions, Where do we come from? What are we? Where are we going? Is there life after death? The Egyptian Civilisation, the birth of Jesus Christ, Mohammad, Jehovah and Buddha provides the clearest evidence (if there could be such evidence)

of there being life after death and I might add that I agree with Wallace, the complexity of the human brain is completely different from that of the chimpanzee who is according to the theory of natural evolution mankind's forefather."

There was a huge smile on Len's face; a hint of tears in his eyes, his voice was soft and gentle.

"Abstract thoughts mirror the soul Henry; they are the essence of our being, perhaps in the final account, they describe us, whom and what we are during the short time we spend on Earth.' He stopped to adjust his scarf, then almost whispering he said. *'Henry, abstract thought is all we have, all we leave behind, mankind's legacy portrayed in numbers, words, monuments, paintings, literature, poetry and music, statements, created and redefined by each generation of human beings that pass through time, it's a way of mankind being immortal."*

There was a beauty in Len's words, their meaning seemed to be amplified. I thought of my father, the stories he told me when I was a child came flooding back, momentarily in my mind I was a child again, a fleeting moment of safeness and wellbeing.

'For every person Henry, who considers the idea of God and creationism as described in the book of Enoch, of fallen angels, giants, spacemen or Atlantians, 'the Gods' who inhabited the Earth, there's an equal number of people, led mainly by academics and scientists who pursue beliefs driven by a different 'supreme being' man himself. 'The God of Science and Reason', 'The God of logical thought' which embraces the chimpanzee as mankind's forefather. The science of the 'Big Bang' and an ever-expanding Universe, populated with billions of stars, dark energy, dark matter and black holes but no room for spirituality. Science is the religion of the material world, where every mortal thing, element and atom is measured, weighed and given a meaning, value and an explanation for its existence."

Len's words reminded me that mythology, folk tales and religious teaching from every part of the world are precious, whilst science provides answers to only what can be seen, heard, smelt, tasted, dissected and analysed. Science describes the fabric of life but It can't answer the question, depicted in Paul Gauguin's` painting, Where do we come from? What are we? Where are we going? Put me in mind of Walt Whitman's famous poem.

('I believe a leaf of grass is no less than the journey work of the stars / and the pismire is equally perfect, and a grain of sand, and the egg of the Wren / and the tree-toad is a chief chef-d'oeuvre for the highest…)

A quote from Jennifer Vanderbles' brilliant first novel, 'Easter Island' reminding me of Walt Whitman's place as the foremost of American Poets. I found Vanderbles' book more akin to my own beliefs and interest in anthropology than those of Charles Darwin. I recall the opening lines of my dissertation whilst at college in Arizona, 'Every blade of grass, every grain of sand, each cloud, raindrop, snowflake and every single human being, is unique, as are the billions of stars that fill our Universe.' I like to think that Walt Whitman would have been pleased with what I had written, I was proud that I had had similar thoughts as him, though of course nothing like as eloquent.

I thought about the giant Moai statues still standing guard on Easter Island and what Len had written about them in a dog-eared notebook, he had kept in his briefcase.

What inspired the people of Easter Island to create these huge statues 13 to 20 feet tall weighing anything between 14 to 20 tons, the largest and unfinished said to be some 69-feet tall and around 270 tons, some of the statues were standing erect, some laying on the ground and others buried up to their waists? Various chapters recorded in the bible, Genesis, Numbers, the Jewish books Enoch and

Judith refer to Nephilim, as the Sons of God also known as Fallen Angels who mated with women to bring forth a tribe of giants that walked the Earth and then having enraged God, were subsequently destroyed by him in the great flood. Could these giants have lived or taken refuge in Easter Island? A remote island some 2,000 miles west of Chile, an island formed mainly from volcanic lava bursting out of the ocean millions of years ago, 63 square miles of barren land. Are the Moai statues proof of the giants who may have inhabited Easter Island? How strange they look, with their vacant expressions, standing around the perimeter of the Island looking inwards to a barren land, had Gauguin visited the island he might have asked, where did they come from?

I had read Rand Flem-ath and Colin Wilsons book 'The Atlantis Blueprint' waiting with bated breath to see if they would agree with my thoughts of giants inhabiting Easter Island in the chapter 'Fallen Angels' no such luck, there was a lot of detail about fallen angels and a reference to Easter Island as being one of the prime sacred sites in the world but nothing linking the giants referred to by Enoch with the Moai statues at Easter Island, at the time I was disappointed but , that said, the book was thrilling, wonderful research, written with passion, a must-read for anyone interested in adventure and the evolution of mankind. Interestingly Eric Von Daniken's name pops up again. Daniken had made reference to Aliens visiting Easter Island in his book 'The Chariots of the Gods' but his supporting evidence was said at the time to be shaky. However this should not weaken the fact that the giant Moia are witness to something very odd that happened on Easter Island for which there is no plausible explanation.

The reference to Easter Island being a prime sacred site by Rand Flem-ath and Colin Wilson confirmed to me that Easter Island and its Moai residents were a key to mankind's past. How to unlock the door to the past, that was the challenge.

I had also had sight of Thor Heyerdahl's account of his

expeditions to American in nothing more than a reed boat. The adventure across the Atlantic ocean in a reed boat similar to those referred to on the walls of Egyptian tombs makes compelling reading; Thor Heyerdahl was able to draw a line of passage from Egypt sailing across the Atlantic Ocean to America, Mexico and Peru where reed boats had also been found. Fallen angels, visitors from Egypt thousands of years ago suggested an evolution of a totally different kind than what Darwin had posed and had nothing to do with chimpanzees. Thor had inadvertently found a key to the past, to a mystery on a tiny island in the Pacific ocean, home to the Moai, murals of bird headed men, reed boats and its earliest inhabitants who worshiped Ra. Thor's journey didn't prove Egypt exported their beliefs to the Americas but it was a huge step forward and could not be ignored.

Likewise so is the sculpture of four giant Pharaohs cut into the rock face, still standing guard over the tombs they are buried in the valley of the kings at Thebes some four thousand years after they were sculpted, and the Sphinx some years older than her neighbour the great pyramid of Cheops gazing with her emetic smile that crosses the desert. Beneath the body of the Sphinx it is said there are vaults that contain the secrets of our past and answers to our questions 'where are we going' but still we search in vain, whilst these ancient monuments stand in defiance of the anthropologist and scientists with their radio carbon dating equipment, centrifuges, microscopes and computers, programmed to define and categorise these huge monuments into a 'Darwinian' concept of 'natural evolution' whilst Hubble, mankind's mechanical Time Lord, scans the Universe in search of new and dead stars, attempting to map and define the edge of an ever changing Universe and everything within it.

Eleven

Giza, Egypt 20th January 2012

Len moved on to another subject dear to his heart, I found the notes behind a drawer in the sideboard.

In CERN, Switzerland close to the border with France buried deep in the ground, the ultimate scientific experiment or folly in 'abstract thought' is taking place. A group of scientists spend their time, watching atoms smashing into each other in a giant temperature-controlled circular tunnel called a collider, measuring around 26 miles in circumference. Scientists claim to have found the 'Higgs Boson subatomic particle'; they call it 'The God particle' that created the big bang and is the life force of every living being. I recall reading that at the time of the 'big bang' temperatures reached thousands of degrees as the Universe came into being. At CERN the same conditions cannot be re-created. For one thing, the sensing equipment would melt or explode, during the experiment, if the same temperatures as the big bang was said to have created, hence the need for temperature control, to my mind this is a basic flaw in this experiment. There is also the size of the collider to consider, simulating the big bang; the collider is minuscule compared to the size of the universe, it's nonsense, colour code red.

Len had written at the bottom of the page in red, capital letters:

'AS IF'

My head was spinning, there was too much to analyse. For the scientist, it's so different, there's always something new to conquer, facts to establish, papers to write as they argue and jostle amongst themselves for fame, glory and immortality. I quote from a different set of notes.

From the rarefied atmosphere of academic understanding, the Scientists come down from the ivory towers where they reside, in their hands they carry their proofs, computer print outs, behind them wagons carrying hundreds and thousands of pages, containing trillions of calculations. The modern-day version of Moses ten commandments, mesmerised by their shinny bound presentation, the wealth of detail and sheer complexity overwhelm us, blindly, silently we accept the 'new commandments' regarding the Big Bang, where we came from, where we are going, what we must now, think and believe. 'Atheism' is the new religion; we no longer live in fear of damnation and life after death a living hello. Freedom of fear comes at a price, being that we are spiritually dead at birth until we die. Those that retain their godly faith, realise the scientists' 'new commandments' are no more than pieces of paper that are unlikely to have been read, other than the headline and would take an auditor several lifetimes to verify.

Perhaps in an ironic way, the activities in CERN underpin atheism, the ultimate folly of abstract thought, though lurking in the shadows, sinister but more plausible, Mary Shelley's monster Frankenstein awaits re-birth, bigger and better than the original. The new monster is complete with bionic moving hands, stem cell body parts, helium-filled superconductors and circuitry, embedded memory chips and the all-important the 'God particles', encapsulated like a third eye in the centre of the monster's forehead, all neatly covered with culture-grown pigskin. To make Frankenstein more personable the creature is dressed in a white shirt, Eaton, old school tie, pinstriped suit, leather brogues, his huge head supported by silver bars passing through its body and fastened to the creature's hips. The monster has the same vacant look of the Moai of Easter Island. In a laboratory linked to a giant accelerator hidden from human view, not far from CERN, a hungry new age Nazi scientist with gleaming eyes, face mask and rubber-gloved hands stands beside the isolator switch, ready and waiting to activate the beast.

"Just give me the word Victor."

He begs Doctor Stein, the project commander who for one moment looks unsure, then nods his agreement to proceed. A thin smile traces Doctor Stein lips, careful that his instructions to activate the monster were not spoken or recorded in writing, the lab was bugged and CCTV cameras captured on film everyone who came in and went out, a nod of the head will suffice. The 'dark angel' the monsters real creator and its master, sits in a cavern miles beneath the surface of the Earth, a look of satisfaction on his face, Doctor Stein has served his purpose, now to business to destroy all that is good in the world, let evil reign supreme.

I was surprised and concerned at what I was reading, was this Len, the gentle and self-effacing mathematician I knew, something within him had changed?

What had Len got into? Sometimes my head hurt so much I thought it was going to explode, too much information, I wanted to stop. But for Len like his fellow mathematicians and scientists, there was never enough time or enough new material to be analysed. I realise now, we should have stopped there. To my mind, we had achieved enough but at Len's insistence, we changed course, leading us to another path that ran alongside his interest in the Universe. I could tell listening to Len that the concept of what he called bad science was an anathema to him.

From childhood, he had immersed himself in the world of science and mathematics. He had a brilliant mind but unlike some mathematicians, his mind was not closed to the possibility that some of the maths or the values assigned could be wrong or out of context; right or wrong, in the end, he gave his life in the pursuit of his beliefs.

It was very different for me. I grew up on the

homestead; my family were part of a small tribe of Native North American Indians living in what we believed were sacred lands of Arizona. We weren't taught in the same way as our fellow white Americans. We were taught to see what lies between light and darkness, shadows, form and the formless, seeing for an Indian goes beyond defining the object in front of him and includes respecting ancient beliefs handed down through the generations. Although my father Bald Eagle was a fearless warrior, I remember him saying to me when I finally gained my place to go to University.

"Don't be in too much of a hurry to arrive at your destination Red Feather, you might find you are going in the wrong direction."

Sometimes I could hear his words echoing in my ears; reminding me of the attacks on my integrity by Professor McDonald during my brief time at the University that had shaken my confidence and made me question whether I had made the right decision in coming to Egypt and then agreeing to write up Len's notes at his father's insistence. On a bad day I lacked confidence and needed to know, where was I going?

Good days were a real joy, when we would discuss evolution in general terms, it became easier for Len than for me to consider that there was a gap or something missing in Charles Darwin's theory of natural evolution relating to mankind, which had not been properly addressed, missed or worse just ignored by Darwin and his contemporaries Len realised how easy it was to get so bogged down in any subject matter and to use an old cliché you could miss the wood for the trees, he had written:

My thoughts keep returning back to Darwin and Easter Island, had Darwin missed something obvious? One significant point was that he hadn't visited Easter Island during the Beagles voyage around the southern hemisphere; instead it had sailed to Tahiti and the Galapagos Islands but not Easter Island. Had Darwin visited Easter Island he would have had to consider the presence of the Moai statues, the murals of bird-headed men, along with the reed boats found on the island, what did they symbolise? Where did they fit into his beliefs of natural evolution and the God Ra, which the people on Easter Island worshipped? The same God, Ra that was worshipped by the Pharaohs in Egypt and the Indians in Peru. Darwin might have dismissed these findings as coincidences, more religious mumbo jumbo, but science does not like or tolerate coincidences, in truth I don't believe Darwin did either and neither do I. So where does Easter Island leave us.

There is very little known about Easter Island, it's an enigma it has been speculated that is was one of the first places on Earth to be inhabited by life some anthropologists speculated that Easter Island was not inhabited by humans until the fourteenth century AD though Len had already suggested that the giant Moai sculptures depict a race of giants inhabiting Easter Island. Looking critically at someone else's work in hindsight, is not the same as having the original idea or even having a different idea but not visiting Easter Island I think was a serious omission by Darwin though perhaps not of his making, the ports of call may have been defined by HM Government and the Admiralty.

It is worth noting that there are some 20,000 to 30,000 islands in the Pacific Ocean, it is difficult to think that Galapagos was any more unique or different than any of the multitude of islands in the Pacific, though Easter Island certainly was. Easter Island, Pitcairn, and Gambieri, were all within reach of the Beagle during the voyage. How strange that the giant Moai statues and reed boats, perhaps the greatest clue to another form of life have been found only on one remote island in the Pacific Ocean and not to my mind, part of any natural evolution, a total mystery. Len wrote stubbornly on:

This omission or at best, a lost opportunity led me to think something important had been missed and if so perhaps the evidence of natural evolution was not so cut and dried as modern anthropologists would have us believe.

I was beginning to question myself again, could religious belief and creationism be woven into one fabric going someway to answering the questions posed by Charles Darwin, Alfred Wallace, Robert Fitzroy, Paul Gauguin, Thor Heyerdahl and now ourselves?

Interestingly both Darwin and Gauguin for different reasons spent time in Tahiti. Darwin when he went on his famous voyage on the Beagle 1831-1836 accompanying Fitzroy who was the ship's Captain and a keen anthropologist himself and then Gauguin disillusioned with life in France sailed to Tahiti in 1891 where he painted profusely and wrote a book Noa Noa, then returning to France only to set sail again for Tahiti in 1895 this time never to return to France. Gauguin's painting 'The Spirit of the Dead' has an eerie echo of the Egyptian 'Ba' the human-headed bird standing guard over a dead woman, illustrated in 'The book of the dead'. His painting another clue or a question what happens when we die?

Sadly Gauguin died in agony in 1903 just prior to having to spend a month in prison for allegedly libelling the Governor of Tahiti, he was 54 years old, fame did not come until after his death, his most famous painting being, 'Where do we come from? What are we? Where are we going?'

Len's notes suggested to me that Gauguin died a troubled soul. The nineteenth century was the time when the issue of creationism as opposed to natural evolution came to a head; it fascinated Len, the different opinions of the chief protagonists opposing each other. In addition to

Len's narration, there were various notes on separate pieces of paper and the computer but none of them tied together, this was my task, to put his words and ideas together.

It was the title of his famous painting, 'Where do we come from? What are we? Where are we going? That generated my initial interest in Creationism, Darwinism and natural evolution. Charles Darwin on completion of the Beagles voyage returned to Falmouth in a blaze of glory, rightly so, his work and the way he gathered and noted his samples showed him to be a great anthropologist as well as a great writer, we need to remember that he was only twenty-two years old when the voyage commenced, on his return, a man older than his years, stood with greatness awaiting.

Fitzroy on the other hand though being awarded the gold medal from the Royal Geological Society in 1837 for his research during the voyage walked in Darwin's shadow, his geological findings went mainly unnoticed by the general public, though he published his work in four volumes as well as a small book 'Remarks' with reference to the Deluge, which confirmed in his mind the events of the great flood in the book of Genesis.

There is considerable merit in Fitzroy's observations; he had provided a comprehensive selection of samples during the voyage. Fitzroy claimed that it was the location of shells above the current water line as being the evidence that much of the land at one time had been covered by water, underpinning the recordings of the Great Flood, he would have made a good detective. Fitzroy had other theories of note and questioned the reference in the bible to the length of the days in which God created the world, something I myself have considered. A day in God's time might be anything, from 24 hours, a year a thousand years, we need to acknowledge that at the time God created the Universe as recorded in the bible is arbitrary.

Fitzroy on his return from the voyage retained his Christian faith to Darwin's disappointment. He married in 1836 and became a member of parliament in 1841 and then Governor of New Zealand, becoming exhausted and depressed; he committed suicide in April of 1865, what a tragic end to life. In contrast, Charles Darwin on his return to England began developing his theories on the origin of the species. It would be another twenty-two years before his work was published. It might have been longer if it had not been for Alfred Wallace who was ready to publish his own papers on natural evolution. Alfred Wallace was a younger man and came from a notably poorer background than Darwin, there was an exchange of letters and the theories were published simultaneously, though it was Darwin that took the plaudits.

With the publication of their work on evolution, a perfect storm was brewing; the Church of England became alarmed and had to refute Darwin and Wallace's claims regarding natural evolution in a way that would kill them off. For the advocates of natural evolution, the new concept needed to take a greater hold, they had to confront the church establishment head-on, not just stand its ground but gain ground and move forward. Thomas Huxley, a young and up and coming English scientist, after some initial doubts, became the champion of 'Darwinism', a term still used today. The stage for the meeting was at Oxford, where a debate on the subject was set up.

There are many accounts as to what Samuel Wilberforce the Bishop of Bristol (for the church) and Thomas Huxley (on Darwin's behalf) said to each other about being descended from Apes but the outcome was clear, Huxley had clearly bettered Wilberforce in the debate. The result being that Christian doctrine and the church suffered a considerable blow to its credibility, whilst the concept of natural evolution, 'Darwinism' took a firmer hold. Huxley had arrived and went on to become a leading scientist of his day. As the nineteenth century folded into the twentieth-century scientific research and understanding in astrology, geology, biology grew rapidly as more discoveries were being made, whilst the church (then and to the current day) remained on the back foot. In scientific terms the church had the difficulty of having to prove a negative, (producing to a sceptic public an invisible God) and unable to challenge the ever growing science with its old and vulnerable claims for creationism, when science had so many overwhelming solid proofs regarding the origin of the Universe, Earth and mankind. The one glimmer of hope for the church was that no one, not even a scientist could disprove God's existence being the other side of the argument which scientists sometimes choose to ignore. It was Charles Lyell's book 'Principles of Geology' published 1831-33 that made the initial case for natural evolution depicting Uniformitarian's, 'changes in the earth surface', as the proof that the Earth must be much older than had been initially thought. Lyell initially in Darwin's camp was torn between Creationism and Natural Evolution, his support for the later was never more than lukewarm, he was not alone.

The Darwinists that followed Thomas Huxley did not have things all their own way in their relentless challenge against creationism. As well as Alfred Wallace who changed his mind on the link between Chimpanzee and humans, there was Robert Fitzroy the Captain of the Beagle who did not accept Darwin's theories of evolution. It seems so strange that whilst they shared five years at sea together, Darwin and Fitzroy on their return to England would have such diverse opinions on the subject of natural evolution. By the mid-twentieth century Lynn Margulis a microbiologist came up with a theory that 'Inherited variations do not come in part or full from random mutations', her publication 'The Journal of Theoretical Biology' was met with a stony silence and was comprehensively rejected by the scientists of the day, undeterred she pressed on and published 'The Origin of Eukaryotic cells' and then produced a trump card, her book reworked and re-titled 'Symbiosis in cell evolution' which became a textbook classic, interestingly with James Lovelock the 'Gaia theory' was developed suggesting that the Earth's atmosphere, climate, organisms and the geology of the Earth created a 'steady state' whereby life on Earth could be maintained.

The structure of cells was way, way above my head, but the Gaia theory, it seemed to me was a link to creationism.

It also showed how fickle scientists can be and gave me renewed heart and the strength to complete Len's research, included below is a page I found in his briefcase, it indicates the direction he was taking.

As well as trying to refute the science of natural evolution, materialism also took hold, challenging the church and Christianity with values and quality of life measured by what we have. Money and greed have become a religion in their own right, sadly science cannot come to the rescue of the new creed it helped to create, its Universities and Laboratories and many scientists need the financial benefactor's money to survive.

In many developed countries especially in Europe and America, we have jobs, material wealth, homes, food, water, welfare education and every type of entertainment you can name but we do not seem content there's an absence of wellness. The ingredients that make us whole love, compassion, kindness and spiritualism (a belief in God) seem to be lacking, nothing to bond with! We have become disconnected.

On another piece of paper Len had written in bold capital letters:

WE'VE STOPPED BELIEVING IN GOD!!!

And then returning to his squiggly lower case,

Or perhaps surrounded by wealth, seeking fame and immortality, we believe 'we are God' how apt Andy Warhol's quote, "In the future, everyone will be world-famous for 15 minutes." When we all get to play God for 15 minutes, illustrated by his own silkscreen prints, masquerading as art, Andy Warhol had longer than the allotted 15 minutes but only just. Saying this I have to acknowledge that like or dislike Warhol's work, his prints of Chairman Mao, Marylyn Monroe and Elvis alongside innocuous tins of soup, are 'art' but to my mind his work is synthetic, ideas developed by printers to create and illustrate the desired effect, yes it's art, but it's a billion miles away from the magnificence of the sphinx 2,500 BC, the great pyramid Cheops 2,500 BC and the treasures of Tutankhamen's tomb 1,332 BC.

Warhol's greatest contribution to the arts, was to make us question what art is, its value and meaning, he didn't need to be a great artist himself (and wasn't) to set in process this school of thought, in reality it needed someone like him who was not a great artist to beg the question. What has followed is a shallowness and thinness in art reliant on computers to convey the artist's ideas. Like the scientist who waits for the computer programs to provide the calculations that prove his theory's, the artist stands beside a printer that produces his work in limited editions, to give the work authenticity and financial value, the prints are signed and numbered by the artist, Warhol had made his point, 15 minutes the allotted time is long enough to endure thin art. Stretched canvas; pens, pencils paints, easels, the famous and obligatory north lights are things of the past, and long forgotten. Music with tone and voice modelling controlled by the computer's programs, ensure perfect pitch and eliminate what it perceives as the singer's duff notes. I guess I am old fashioned, but I think the reliance on computer technology does little for the development of an artist and even less for our future as thinking, spiritual human beings.

It was a strange end to these notes but when I asked if he was okay Len replied.

"Yes."

I could tell he was really excited with the progress he was making, though he didn't want to push on with this line of research, instead, he wanted to check some issues he had regarding mathematics, saying:

"These essential tools used to describe, prove and quantify the scientific research and data upon which academic knowledge is formulated needed to be reviewed."

Twelve

Giza, Egypt February 2012

The following notes bring together several aspects of Len's thoughts on mathematics. Len's father had requested that I write up the unfinished notes and collate Len's papers into some order. At the time, I felt privileged to be asked to undertake such a task, little realising how much work was involved; now, at times it was a nightmare. The actual typing, editing and the like I did not mind too much, but the meat in the sandwich, what Len actually thought left me flummoxed, I wasn't in his league, the importance of what he said and wrote was lost on me. Sometimes I felt I was a fraud, my name sitting beside his. Len's work was too important to be put together by an amateur and I was that man. There were hundreds of pieces of paper, containing calculations fragments of ideas, drawings and sketches, news cuttings and theorems as well as numerous essays in various stages of completion on his laptop.

I had printed most of his notes off and indexed everything, the handwritten and the work on the computer together with the research papers. Some of his ideas I could follow but many of them I couldn't begin to understand. I indexed and archived the papers as best I could, mainly by date order, copying the ones I needed for the book and then returning them to Len's father in England. The gist of his unique thoughts on Zero are set out below. Len placed 'abstract thought' high on the list of mankind's behaviour, a term he used that identified and marked out the difference between humans from other animals and life forms on Earth. His ideas can be further illustrated by the concept of zero actually existing. On a slip of paper Len had written:

It is my belief that zero can be seen, felt, observed, measured and defined, rather than as described in books and integral to modern mathematics. To summarise our understanding of Zero, it's a number that has no value or is the sum of nothingness. For me zero is an integral part of defining time, temperature, speed and motion, the starting point of numbers and measurement.

On another piece of paper Len had written:

The theories and use of zero have both terrified and fascinated mathematicians and scientists alike for thousands of years. Records indicate zero as a number first came into being about 8,000 years ago, given that mankind had been around between 100,000 to 200,000 years if you accepted Charles Darwin's theory of natural evolution, brought me to the conclusion that zero was not and never would be essential to mankind's actual existence, a point borne out by the primitive tribes of Indians living mainly in South America, whose way of life has remained much the same for thousands and thousands of years where there is no need of zero as a number or as a concept.

And from his laptop under the file name 'Abstract Thoughts':

Zero, is the perfect example of abstract thought. It has been purposely built into our psyche from childhood by teachers and academics as having an important meaning and essential to our way of life. Most of us first come across zero when learning geometry and algebra for solving complex mathematical problems. Fast forward to today's world and we can see that Computers and much of the digital technology providing the fabric of modern life could not exist without zero being an integral part of their design and programming.

One of Len's essays talks about the number of books and different theories that have been written about zero, he wrote:

I have become intrigued by Karl Sabbagh's book, Doctor Riemann Zeros, Sabbagh describes the enigma of prime numbers and the pattern of zeros occurring on the zeta line. Outside of the rarefied atmosphere of pure mathematics, practiced at Princeton and other universities around the world, the concept of zero, together with the speed of light, string theories and the fourth dimension are part of the daily diet that feeds the mathematician's abstract thought. In the everyday world of ordinary people, Teachers, Bankers, Designers and Computer Programmers, use zero simply as a tool in their lives without question to its value. Zero is just an accepted part of the fabric of modern life.

The best example of Zero is expressed by a bank statement that indicates you have no money in the bank, zero money, perhaps at that moment in time you don't have a bank account any more or you have a negative balance where you owe money. That's one of the problems with Zero, it can be used as a play on words, how can it exist if you can never see it? Or if you accept that numbers begin at 1,2,3,4 etc then 0 must exist as the number before 1 and so the argument goes on. There are people who question zeros existence or if it does exist what is its use? Countered by the rational of 'where would we be if zero was used as a number' if it 'didn't exist' or 'was not used' in mathematics? How would we express the value of nothing? Or more challenging, what if zero could be shown to have a value?

In one of Len's of papers I found in his bedside drawer, he had written:

Zero exists! I expect most people will say this is madness, it's unthinkable and could never be accepted other than at Princeton or Stanford.

I am sure the Professors of mathematics who reside in such places spending their lives engrossed in 'abstract thought' will confirm my findings and can explain if you are able to understand the obscure sign language of mathematics, scrawled on to blackboards and note pads that everything is possible including 'zero as having a value' in the world of pure mathematics.

Turning the piece of paper over he had written:

With the use of the most powerful computers, the impossible can be made to seem possible. An example being the largest prime number found to date, comprising more than 22.5million digits, more than the number of individual letters/digits in this thesis. In reality, the largest prime number is physically un-readable.

I did the math, to put Len's example into perspective, there are approximately 2950 individual digits on a page of these notes, there are 129 pages in total, making a total of around 3,628,623 digits, a further 7726 or so pages would be needed to write out the largest prime number in written format. Are we any wiser for knowing this? At the bottom of the piece of paper Len had scrawled:

It's hard to believe that somewhere on our planet there are people, sitting beside gigantic computers, roaming the universe of pure mathematics for new prime numbers, their lives given to finding a number which no one can see and only faintly imagine. Adding.

The biggest prime other than it exists is questionable, what is certain is that sometime in the future a larger prime will be found and hundreds of pieces of paper required if it is to be recorded as an actual number, an example of 'abstract thought' at its best and most meaningless.

The notes ended abruptly with *'where are we going?'* written in red.

The concept of zero as having 'no value' or 'nothingness' had always bothered Len. Zero came up in an odd and unforeseen way. Browsing in a small bookshop in Giza one afternoon, Len found a worn copy of Karl Sabbagh's book 'Dr Riemann's zero's, he had also read an article about 'zero' in a computer magazine. Len's initial interest in the value of zero dated back to when he was a student at Oxford but for some reason he had lost interest and it had lain dormant in his mind until this particular day, his interest was renewed reading Sabbagh's book. Intrigued by Riemann's theorem, the adrenalin rush sped through Len's veins, the excitement of pure mathematics had returned.

He spent a great deal of time trying to establish what he termed 'the real value of zero' as being more than just a number or a figure of speech with little meaning. He came in one day holding Sabbagh's book in his hand, looking agitated, his face was a ruddy red colour, he looked as if he was about to explode.

"I wish he wouldn't do this Henry."

Len said, pushing the book under my nose. I looked at him, his eyes were blood shot, he had been crying, his hair an unwashed tangled mess; I got him to sit down and poured him a large scotch and soda. I had never seen him so distressed.

"Who wouldn't do what Len?" I replied.

"Them, they speak in riddles, look."

He said pointing to a page, tears running down his face, jabbing with his forefinger, clearly angry.

"Sabbagh asks me to imagine a road of infinite numbers beginning with zero to illustrate and identify the location of prime numbers along its length. To make the analogy easier to understand he says, each prime can be identified as a house, the first prime being house number 1 then 3, 5, 7, 11 and so on, the road of houses stretches into infinity with each new prime found."

"What's wrong with that Len?"

He gave me that curious grimace of his, as if I was the most stupid person on the planet. His contorted face usually made me smile or sometimes laugh, this time; I bit my lip, as he wiped the tears away with his sleeve.

"The house numbers don't start at zero, Henry"

He was still crying with frustration. I could see how wretched it was for him.

"They never could, why say one thing and then say something quite different, it isn't fair?"

"And that's what's making you angry?" I said, relieved to see the anger was dissipating as fast as it had arisen, he was calming down but anything which did not fit into his concept of numbers and zero, in particular, had become a flashpoint. I notice over the past week or so, everything was black or white, right or wrong, in Len's mind everything had to be perfect, he would tolerate nothing less.

"What you are saying Len, is that a line, defined in length by numbers, can't begin with zero, because zero doesn't exist in real space, it's only theoretical."

"Exactly."

He smiled, it was his way of apologising for the outburst, adding.

"Sabbagh's line of houses seems to tell us that."

Thank God I wasn't a mathematician, they had brilliant minds but no mental strength, I went through to the kitchen and made some tea, leaving Len pacing up and down.

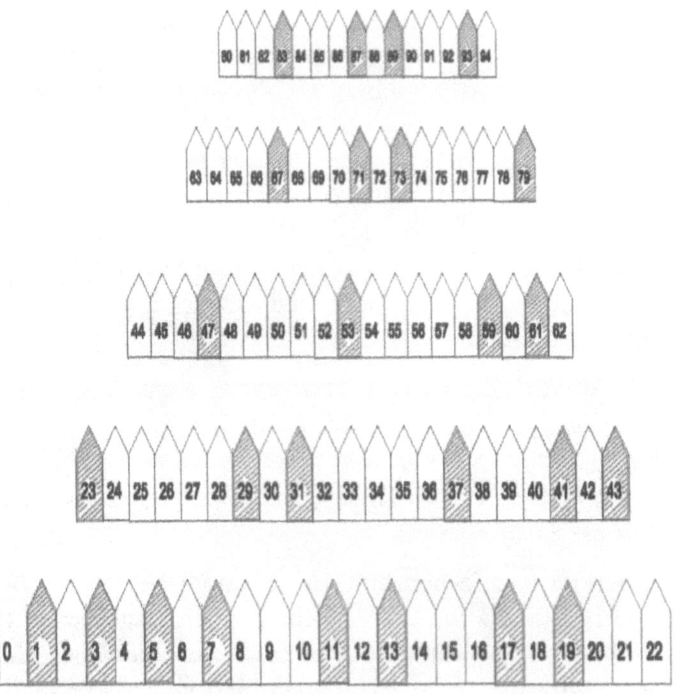

**In the above example, prime numbers (shaded) are part
of a street beginning with 1 to infinity.
Although shown, zero is not a number.**

Another way to explain Len's thoughts relating to zero is to refer to his notes on the Celsius scale for measuring the temperature of water. The notes were still on his computer in the folder marked Zero. He had written:

First discovered by Anders Celsius in 1744, centigrade as it was called then, defined the freezing point of water as zero degrees centigrade and 100 degrees centigrade as the boiling point of water. The current Celsius scale incorporates two different points. Absolute zero defined as minus 273.15 degree centigrade and the triple point VSMOW.

From what Len had written, there were two issues which did not sit easy in his mind. First, he did not like the term 'absolute zero' and hated 'minus numbers' used so much in mathematics, saying 'minus numbers' were too abstract and far too theoretical. Secondly, he did not accept that the change in water changing from ice (solid form) to water (liquid form) being described as zero, it was, he said too arbitrary, adding:

"If there had to be a scale for measuring the temperature of water which also defines absolute zero, then I suggest the lowest temperature should begin at zero, then one and moved forward numerically when ice became water as 273.15 degrees c and changed again from water to steam at 373.15 degrees c."

There was another and more important issue that nagged Len, being the exact moment when water becomes ice and also when water changes to steam. On the Celsius scale, the formation of ice is identified as zero with the temperature decreasing in minus numbers as ice intensifies in its frozen state. The point Len wanted to make, was that there must be a moment when the element was neither water nor ice and at the other end of the scale, neither water or steam, the problem with numbers and fractions of a whole number was that they were 'infinite' and consequently un-measurable, Len said:

"The actual melting point of ice when it becomes water is 0.000,089 (10) degrees Celsius."

Len was really excited when he explained to me where this research was going, he said:

"The point where water is neither ice in its frozen state or water in its liquid state was zero, 'the space' between the two separate

conditions."

Adding.

"Ice is identified as -1

Neither ice nor water the value 0 (Zero)

And

Water given the value +1."

This simple logic satisfied two different aspects of zero which had always bothered Len.

First, it illustrated the anomaly of numbers commencing with zero and secondly and importantly in the example quoted, gave zero a tangible value in the real world a logical place in numerology and the theoretical world of mathematics. Whether other mathematicians would accept his logic was never an issue for Len, what eminent professors and students of mathematicians thought, more learned than him, was of no consequence, Len pursued his theories in singular fashion in the manner of Dirac and Gauss, his boyhood heroes. Len was a loner absorbed only with his thoughts rather than those of his contemporaries, I loved this quote, it summed him up so clearly.

Zero is the number (value) which exists between plus 1 and minus 1 the example of this is shown in the diagram below, where each block representing a series of plus and minus numbers is given. Zero is the space between the plus and minus numbers that is the moment between something and nothing. In the case of ice changing into water, it could be said that zero = 0.000,001 (10) degrees Celsius. A side issue of the Celsius scale was the reference to absolute zero being minus 273.15. Len had already found many examples of the English language which he said was a play on words and numbers, used sometimes by scientists to make the simple complicated and sometimes used to describe the indescribable.

I returned to the notes which contributed to Len's latest seizure.

Scientists in Helsinki claim they have actually measured the temperature of a rare metal to within a tenth of a billionth of a degree above minus 273.15 Celsius wow! I find this new research interesting but also worrying, similar to prime numbers the largest number found to date comprising 22.5 million digits. These numbers are too complex for people to understand, scientists need to realise these facts (if that is what they are) they have little meaning for ordinary people. In another line of research, I read that 'Helium 4' forms into a liquid when cooled to within 2 thousands of a degree Celsius above 'absolute zero' which has been termed 'a superfluid' that opens the way for the development of super-conductors in our computer-generated age. But how would liquid helium behave at the temperature of absolute zero? Where there is no movement and objects are inert and lifeless, stilled to death and frozen in time. Is it possible to detect movement or oscillation of an object at absolute zero?

If we knew Helium 4 could be turned into a fluid at -273.15 'absolute zero', a whole new science would be born! A concern comes to mind, would the equipment that records these extremely low temperatures begin to slow down or falter as it measures objects at absolute zero? My God, what if!!! What if Helium 4 flourishes as a liquid at absolute zero if this were so, it changes everything. A further point for consideration, if nothing moves at absolute zero Celsius 'as in space', how does the Universe expand or put another way, if nothing moves and the Universe still expands, then, 'zero must have a value' but how do we verify any of this?

The truth is that whilst many facts have been established about the size, composition and age of stars and galaxies the nearest star being trillions of miles from Earth, we know very little of the composition of space, which has been described as: made of particles of dust, together with gases, liquids and the residue of the 'big bang' *through which light, sound and radiation pass. Another school of thought suggest, that space is a vacuum in which all the stars, galaxies and black holes are suspended, swathes of dark matter, dark energy, anti-matter combined with dust, liquids and gases swirling into the infinite to places that we will never see. Rather than studying the stars and galaxies, I suggest the make up and composition of 'space' is the key to our understanding of the Universes and its creation. My view is that the composition of space is similar to the Earths atmosphere, though less dense, a mixture of gas, liquid and dust but much thinner than our atmosphere and as has been predicted extremely cold, (can we measure to within a degree Celsius in space that is trillions and trillions of miles from Earth?) I doubt it, but space must be something more tangible than dark matter, dark energy and antimatter, descriptions which have little or no real meaning. If the Universe is expanding, then we need to know what 'space' is comprised of and what the <u>Universe</u> is expanding into.*

The notes ended abruptly, followed by a poem Len had written:

THE SACRED NUMBER

*The phantom of mathematics stands astride the Earth's
    north pole*

*His giant torso clad in sable and ermine reaching miles
    into the sky*

His leaden arms held aloft, facing east

The palms of his hands

open and outstretched

Blocking the sun's rays casting two huge circular shadows

that cross each other at 12 noon, midday

forming a golden number 8 in a cloudless sky.

For three days the phantom stands silently in awe

Facing the Universe and its creator

Forming two more golden numbers

Then the phantom vanishes, never to be seen again.

But the three golden numbers remain

Figures of eight, aligned side by side

gleaming in the midnight sky

form another number

888

The sacred number

The number of Jesus Christ.

Len had scrawled a note below the poem in red ink:
Please, God let it be true, that Zero has a tangible value?

Thirteen

Giza, Egypt March 2012

When I returned to the flat, Len was slumped on his chair; he had been sick and was crying. He looked up imploringly at me trying to muster a smile and speak but began coughing as more bile came from his mouth.

"Hey, take it easy, let's get you cleaned up."

I took him to the bathroom, ran a bath and put his clothes in the washing machine; I could hear him mumbling incoherently about Helium and Zero as he bathed himself. An hour and two stiff whiskies later he went to bed. I sat with him whilst he insisted on explaining that Helium 4 was the key to zeros existence, saying that in the moment of discovery, he had become overexcited, delirious and then sick. I left him to sleep, if he was no better in the morning I would ring for a Doctor. I was tired but copied his notes over to my laptop, then Googled 888 typing in the number. There were several references in scriptures to the number 888 linking it to Jesus Christ. The words that relate to the number 888 that stood out for me can be found in Malachi 3.6 (I am the Lord, I change not).

John Michelle made reference to the sacred number in his book view over Atlantis; he also wrote other books including works on Sacred Geometry. I thought about the link between numbers, written words but more importantly spoken words and their value to each other. The sound of a word has a resonance that can be measured and given a value. Great and powerful words lodge in the mind can inspire us to great deeds; they comfort us, express love, reach and energise the soul. As the time of the Egyptian Empire between 4,500 BC to 2,500 BC numerologists developed a science where the structure of sound was established and given a numerical value, sacred sounds were identified, spoken and sung in sacred places where the buildings were set out to sacred measurements. The sounds interact with each other, enhancing the value and spirituality of each. The object being to create perfect harmony, a place, where they were at one with their God. Later drinking a beer, I began to wonder if Len had really identified Zero as having a value or was his mind beginning to wonder, lost in the complex world of mathematics.

Finishing the beer, I got ready for bed; my concern was not about helium, sacred numbers or zero but mainly Len's health and his fragile state of mind. The next day Len seemed refreshed and ready to go, as if the illness the night before hadn't occurred, he showed me some ideas he had compiled, a new form of measuring temperatures which did away with the minus numbers that he hated so much, handing me a reef of papers describing the new scale, I had to smile.

Len had modified the Celsius scale, beginning with the most frozen state 1.15 Celsius (absolute zero), then 2, 3, 4, etc.

To 273 Celsius formation of ice

274 Celsius neither ice nor water (zero)

275 Celsius formation of water

375 Celsius water

376 Celsius neither water or steam and

377 Celsius formation of steam

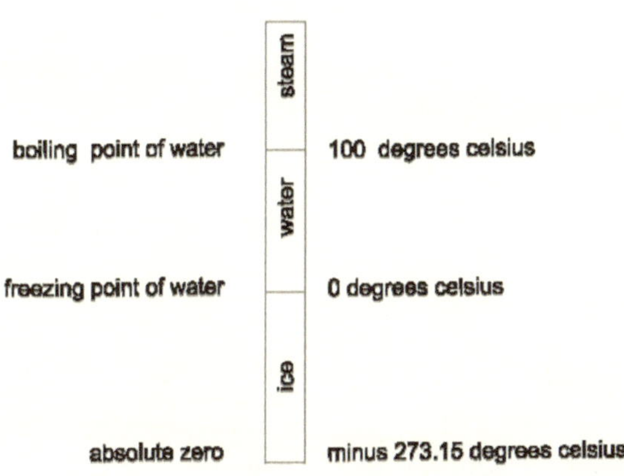

CELSIUS SCALE OF MEASURMENT

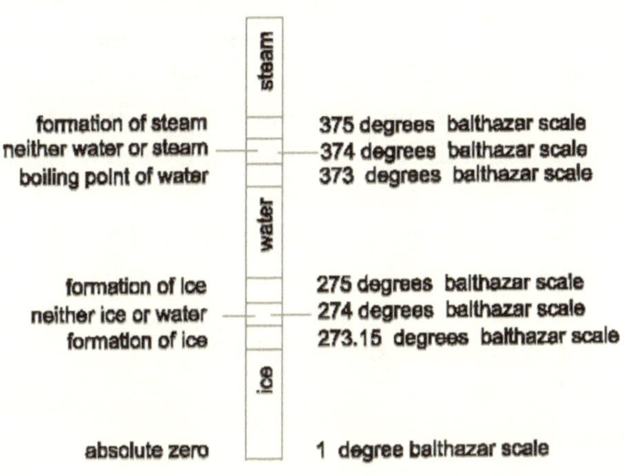

BALTHAZAR SCALE OF MEASUREMENT
The beauty of Balthazar's Scale is that it
eliminates minus numbers

Put another way Len had written:

If zero was to be credible as a way of describing the various states of water, then there should be 4 zeros.

One for the coldest state ice, absolute zero.

One for the state that exists between ice and water, where currently zero is the freezing point. One for the state that exists between water and steam, boiling point.

One for the hottest state of steam, before it condenses back to water.

It sounded simpler and sensible to Len, getting away from minus numbers which he detested and I agreed with. I had other concerns, in the five months I had been living with Len, I began to notice Len's mood swings becoming more unpredictable and that his state of health varied daily. In the main, he seemed to be enjoying the work but as always any interruption or delay caused him to worry. First, he would lose his appetite and then he became restless, agitated and unable to sleep, I began to watch Len intently; I could literally see zeros, swirling around in his eyes as he grappled for a successful explanation. Though numbers and maths were not my real interest, I was excited about Len's research and found the concept of zero as having a real value fascinating, though all I did was listen and make notes.

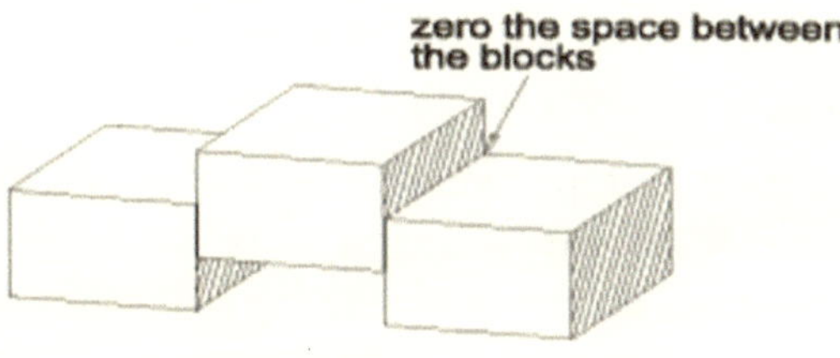

diagram B
three blocks side by side
block 2 shown passing between
blocks 1 & 3

DOES ZERO EXIST?

I began to realise that for Len the research was becoming a life or death struggle, a battle was taking place in his mind. With each day the concept of zero having a tangible value was becoming an obsession. I was alternately angry or worried both with Len and myself, knowing I couldn't help, I was way out of my depth. I listened and tried to steer him into other areas of research but he wouldn't rest without a defined outcome. One positive issue was that we agreed that colour coding had a significant place in qualifying scientific theories. Colour coding words and statements we saw as a vital aid in clarifying various scientific findings; the term 'Absolute zero' was his favourite example which he dismissed, saying he was more interested in the small temperature range in which mankind survived on Earth. Sometimes Len would just say something which came to him at that moment in time.

"Take a bottle of water Henry.' He said laughing. 'If you pour out the water, we say the bottle is empty, but we know the bottle is not empty, the water has just been replaced by the air in the atmosphere. Empty is not the same as zero Henry, mathematics tells us that zero is an absolute and the word empty would also like to be defined as an absolute but it isn't."

Another example which irritated Len was the predicted temperature of the sun and also the beginning of the Universe milliseconds after the big bang. The temperatures are said to have been in the tens of thousands of degrees centigrade or as Steven Hawking suggests measured in trillions of degrees. Though hard to quantify or measure in any meaningful way Len acknowledged the claims were probably correct but couldn't be proved other than by calculation and computer simulation to illustrate their intensity at first hand. He had written:

Using colour coding the claim can be qualified in red, as possible/probable but awaiting physical proof.

Everywhere he looked he came up against abstract theories, computer-driven; he was being overwhelmed with theories which had no tangible meaning or proof.

Having successfully resolved in his mind zero as a defined space or moment between ice and water, Len then turned his mind to the segments that make up a circle which commence with zero degrees and end at 360 degrees. I can remember one evening after a full day's research, exhausted I had gone to bed early, only to be awoken by Len shouting. *'Henry! Henry!"* I looked at my watch; it was just after 2am. As I pulled the covers off the bed Len was banging on the door, shouting.

"Henry I've found another anomaly relating to zero." Living with Len made me realise one thing, he had no concept of time, often working through the night. If he had thought he had woken me up and disturbed my sleep, he would have been mortified. It just hadn't occurred to him that I would be asleep. Getting a coffee for both of us, I made myself comfortable on the settee, now wide awake I listened with interest.

"Henry, if you look at the hour hands of a clock you will see that the beginning of a new day is between 11hours 59minutes-59 seconds and 01 minutes of a second 'am' the following day with midnight being zero."

He looked at me smiling.

"Henry, zero is the time between the end of one day and the beginning of the next day, it exists somewhere between these two timeframes."

I looked at him, then gave him my stupid and exaggerated smile.

"Is this what you have got me up for Len?"

I drank some coffee; Len ignored my comment, getting into full throttle, he said handing me a drawing he had made of a clock face.

"In this example Henry, zero is the beginning and end of time at the same given point which happens every hour of every day of every year in the way we measure time and interestingly if you accept that light travels at 186 miles per second and a nanosecond is 1 billionth of a second then light at the point of 11 hours 59mimutes-59.999,999,999 nanoseconds pm, would have travelled 0.01 inches from the time it would take to record .000,000,001 nanoseconds being the commencement of the new day."

I nodded, but was none the wiser, I realised that for Len this was something of a breakthrough. Whether his research about 'Dr Riemann's zeros was the catalyst which drove Len over the edge, in pursuit of zero as being a part of everything I will never know but to my mind, it led to the illness which caused his untimely death.

Like the clock face, Len noticed that the zero degrees at the top of the circle were covered by a second line drawn at 360 degrees to complete the circle. So that when viewed in 2-dimensional space the line drawn from the centre of a circle to the circumference, zero and 360 degrees occupied the same place in the circle. Something that did not sit easily in Len's mind. The observation was confirmed by the fact that no other numbers which made up the degrees of a circle, clashed with each other in the same way, only the numbers, 0 and 360 occupy the same place on a circle.

Fourteen

Giza, Egypt March 2012

In the following days, Len became increasingly agitated and restless as he strove to resolve the anomalies of zero piling up in his mind. Reading the last notes he was to write on the subject Len had come to the conclusion that zero was the finite space that separated everything from everything else, the minute space between everything, unless everything was one giant homogenous ball of matter forming the Universe, but it wasn't, everything in space was separate from everything else, a chilling thought. Looking back, it is easy to see that Len's mind was both imploding and exploding due to the enormous pressures he was inflicting on himself. A 'big bang' was taking place in Len's brain. I watched helplessly as he grappled with his theory of the edge of the Universe, in a lucid moment towards the end, he said.

"It doesn't expand Henry; I've been to the edge of the Universe with Einstein, Dirac, Hawking and Don Juan." Len was drowning, engulfed in the concept of zero having a tangible value. Perhaps in his imagination or in his dream state, he had glimpsed the edge of the Universe.

There were successes, Len had in his mind been able to identify zero as having a value as in the state between ice and water but sadly he wasn't able to complete his work. His life ended tragically when he suffered a massive brain haemorrhage from which he was never to recover, I remember how I had found him slumped over the computer when I had returned to the flat one evening, within five days he was dead, he was just 26 years old. I tried not to remember Len's death, for various reasons, I felt guilty as if his death had been my fault and though not in blood but in spirit and mind, he was my brother and part of me wanted to die as well. However hard I had tried; I had failed, unable to get him to relax for any real length of time, to get him to see his theories as no more than an interesting pursuit. I told him time and again the issues would be there the next day and the day after, that there was no need to resolve everything in one day but the issues steadily built up in his mind until they overwhelmed him. I should have done more, I should have stopped him but I know now he was never going to be stopped, he wouldn't give up. Writing now I suggest that perhaps like his great Egyptian ancestors, his work will endure but at the time of his death I was in a state of shock and disbelief, even now I find it difficult to come to terms with Len's death. Sometimes I think I can hear his voice in the wind, see his face in the clouds, his presence is always around me. Often when I write, I feel his hand guiding me, his mind inside mine; composing the words he wants me to write to describe his work. At other times his presence was a torment, unable to rid myself of guilt, why didn't I do more to help him? What had I missed? The trail for elusive answers has no end. I have to begin living with what I had or hadn't done remembering the good times we had together and how lucky I had been to know him.

How Len's mother and father came to take him back to England for the funeral. How kind and understanding they were saying. '

"I mustn't blame myself for Len's death, that Len had told them that I was the kindest and most understanding person he had ever met."

I was humbled; it helped me deal with my guilt. Alexander Balthazar had an intensity about him which reminded me of Len. We spoke briefly over the phone, about Len's work and the proposed thesis, it was clear to me he was very proud of his son. I sent him the early proofs of the thesis; He became very excited, writing back.

"It's remarkable Mr Red Feather how you met my son Len, whilst you have many things in common, this is clear." He pointed to the open page on the screen.

"But you are so different in your approach to research so many different ideas."

I smiled saying.

"I didn't do much Mr Balthazar, Len did all the hard work, the thinking and number crunching, and it was an honour to have known your son who counted me as his friend. Len was very gifted."

In one telephone conversation he asked. "Are you okay for money?"

"Yes, fine thanks," I replied.

From the very beginning, I knew I was out of my depth but it was my duty to complete the thesis. I would sit at the table in his apartment typing up his notes, in my mind a clear picture of Len standing in front of me.

"You can do it, Henry, have faith."

Sometimes, standing by the window looking out towards the pyramids and the sphinx, I would ask him what he meant; there were numerous scribbled notes and diagrams, not in any order kept in a shoebox he had kept beside his bed. On the lid, he had written 'IDEAS BOX'.

I recalled that most nights he would wake up, unable to sleep, making his notes on slips of paper. Now coming to the last chapters of the thesis I grew to like the silence working alone in the apartment. It was so peaceful, was it Len or the Sphinx answering my questions, 'all things pass through God's hands Henry', sometimes there was no reply and the eerie silence was terrifying, somehow I managed to complete the work. The outcome of Len's research was that he considered much of the science which form the foundation of mankind's understanding depicted in Paul Gauguin's famous painting, D'Ou Venons nous? Que Sommes Nous? Que Allons Nous? Where do we come from? What are we? Where are we going, was still up for grabs. Len acknowledged that Scientists have a wealth of information regarding the format of the Universe as to 'what happened and when' but he came to the conclusion that Scientists still don't know for sure and probably will never know the whole story. The sticking point being the pre-history of the Universe, what was before the big bang? This is the essential question asked of all of us in the short time we spend on Earth. I remembered my father's words.

"Whatever anyone else tells us Red Feather or insists is correct, the path we as individuals choose to follow and define our understanding of life, are always our own, the proofs we discover for our own satisfaction."

Len had said pretty much the same thing and termed them as value judgements that can be shared.

"Henry the last journey, the end of life on Earth where we encounter physical death, is made alone; the secret of eternal life is taken with death to the grave. When archaeologists come along and open up the coffins of the dead, the skeleton or the mummified body does not reveal if it had a soul and if it had a soul, where it has gone?"

The spells and mysteries which are described in the Egyptian 'Book of the Dead' speak of eternal life.

One thing was certain Len had said,

"It won't be found at the CERN laboratory, bouncing around in a giant accelerator."

His words were ringing in my ears.

Now alone, I was left with the thought that perhaps it is just as well that we never know for sure what happens when we die, until our own time comes, in which case the task of living would not be a challenge if we knew for certain what happens after we die.

Fifteen

Giza, Egypt March 2012

In the final weeks before his death, Len seemed to find new strength and plenty more to give.

"Henry"'

He shouted as he walked across the living room, I could tell when he was about to crack a joke or say something he thought was funny, he would begin laughing, it was never something he could control, I waited.'

"What do God and Black holes have in common?"

Len stood in the middle of the room, slightly stooping, hands in his pockets, he had a Groucho Marks look about him and he couldn't stop laughing, neither could I, his mood was infectious. Trying to control my own laughter I said.

"Ok, tell me then, what have God and black holes have in common."

"You can't see either of them."

His laughter was now out of control as he threw himself on to the settee. It was good to see Len really laughing. After a few minutes he pulled himself together, I sensed he was going to explain what he meant behind the punch line, instead, he burst out laughing again, speaking very slowly and solemnly he said.

"It's not surprising really, the closest supposed black hole is a mere ninety-trillion miles away, it's hardly surprising you can't see

it."

More laugher, then as if he was walking from one room into another his mood changed, he suddenly looked serious.

"Joking apart, there is a serious point here Henry."

"Pad," I replied.

"Yes, let's get this down on paper."

"Ok."

I walked over to the sideboard and picked up a pad and pencil.

"I'm ready Kemah Saby."

"Don't make me start laughing again."

"Humble Indian sit still, not make noise."

My own attempt at a joke was ignored.

"I was looking on Wikipedia and one of the sites that state that V4641 Sagittarii is a binary star system in the constellation of Sagittarius, adding that it is the closest known black hole known to man, which was initially considered to be 1,600 light-years from earth, latter observations indicate that the distance might be more like 24,000 light-years from the earth. Whatever the distance, it was a long way away from Earth. Perhaps the black hole was only 96 trillion miles away; even so, it was visible, now V616 Monocerotis is thought to be the closest black hole. Only 3,000 light-years away and said to be 9 to 13 times the mass of our sun. It's hard to see how anyone can come up with these numbers given that the earth is spinning around the sun and on its own axis whilst the time scaled measurements were being taken, there is also the prospect that V4641and V616 would also be moving across the Universe, direction unknown.

For some reason black holes are popular and have captured our imaginations, people like to believe they exist. A whole new science and technology has grown around the theory of black holes, scientists write of the effect of what happens to the observer, if he falls into a black hole, as if he was taking the next rocket from Nasa for a trip or knew someone that had. Complex theories regarding stellar mass, electron degenerate matter, pathological solutions, surface gravities, event horizons, rotating and non-rotating black holes, ergo spheres and the like populate books, describing the various facets of black holes as if they were discussing a landscape, somewhere not far away that they might visit.

Most diagrams illustrate black holes as having a circumference on a flat surface of swirling matter much like that of a whirlpool from which water disappears as it is sucked into itself at great speed, the water travels around the circumference of the whirlpool, leaving a hole in its centre. The whirlpool is a perfect example of how science jumps from one phenomenon to another because they seem to fit each other. Whirlpools in water, why not black holes in space. All that was needed was for some bright spark to simulate a whirlpool in the Universe, the beauty of this piece of space fiction is that being a black hole you can't see it and disprove its existence, one of the few examples where science is prepared to go along with real proof. What most illustrations do not depict is that a collapsing star implodes in every direction simultaneously becoming as Stephen Hawkings suggests a 'singularity'. The collapsed star would be so dense that no light could escape or be reflected from the object but I do not see how this would form a black hole."

"Does this bother you then Len?"

"Yes."

"Why?"

"You should know why by now."

He pushed his hands through his hair, a sure sign that he was becoming agitated.

"You know Henry, I detest any type of speculation, especially in science, there are even suggestions that black holes can be linked to worm holes when spacecraft, presumably manned by humans go from one to the other. I dread to think how old the spacemen might be, driving through a worm hole and popping up somewhere else in the Universe, some trillions of miles distant."

He pushed his hands through his hair again, sighing.

"It's all such nonsense Henry, it makes my blood boil."

"That's clear then, you don't believe black holes exist."

The humour was gone, in its place a young man, Len, with a ruddy face, looked like he could explode.

"No! Yes, God I don't know."

He walked over to his bedroom and stood in the doorway.

"I don't think I'll bother with dinner, Henry."

I was left to ponder putting the note pad away for another day, glad that I was not a scientist or had any inkling to investigate outer space, tracing the Indian heritage in Arizona was enough for me.

Sixteen

Giza, Egypt April 2012

Unlike Len, I didn't spend too much time considering the possibility of a fourth dimension, if I had thought anything it would have been about dreaming, whether our conscious being is a figment of our imagination whilst we are dreaming or vice versa: it was something I had never properly considered. The subject came to life one morning when Len bushy-tailed for once walked into the lounge.

"I'd like your opinion on this Henry."

As I looked up, Len pushed a bunch of handwritten notes under my nose. He began reading as he went over to the computer.

"2-dimensional space, what we see when we look at a drawing, a painting, read a book, what's written on the blackboard, viewed on a computer screen is expressed as 'A' the length of a 2-dimensional plane multiplied by 'B' the width of the plane to give a field of vision, the area contained in the 2-dimensional plane says, 2M long x 2M wide gives a plane area of 4 square meters.

2-dimensional space always appears flat and we need to remind ourselves when we look at a picture or photograph of a landscape, a group of people in 2-dimensional space, the depth and appearance of 3-dimensional objects, is what we interpret in our minds and imagination and not the 2-dimensional space we are viewing. 3-dimensional space, all that is contained within the physical world can be expressed as 'A' the length of the 3-dimensional space multiplied by 'B' the width multiplied by 'C' the depth of the 3-dimensional space to identify the volume of the space. The space could be a living room, a container holding water, a box or vessel, all the atoms and molecules that form matter, our being, the Earth and ultimately everything in the Universe. The calculations which identify 3-dimensional spaces are provable in physical terms and are understood and used in everyday life. They are the foundations of visual and physical perception. Scientists like these simple equations because they are solid, mathematically provable and dependable, the basis upon which any fourth, fifth or six dimensions of space might follow. For those who have been persuaded and believe some of the claims being made regarding the fourth dimension in the name of Science, the prospect of a whole new world and way of thinking awaits. Perhaps in the fourth dimension time might stand still, everlasting life might be found or like Oscar Wilde's 'Dorian Gray' we remain forever young. Speculation in the halls of Science as to whether the fourth dimension exists is rife, other than in theory 4-dimensional space can't be established. But for those who won't be denied by reality, the fourth dimension can be simulated by computer models where light, time and space can be bent, shaped to mimic the theory.

Following Einstein's Special Theory of Relativity published in 1905 and the work of Hermann Minkowski many scientists believe there is a fourth dimension (space-time) that will enable people to travel through outer space, within their lifetimes, disappearing and re-appearing in some other area of the space which is currently beyond us due to the vastness of the Universe. Star Trek, the famous television series and movie, shows us how we can travel through warped space and worm holes, though in reality this form of space travel is very unlikely to come into being, but for the space travel buffs there is still 'Star Trek' and like many computer modelled theories the concept remains a fascinating possibility."

It was Len's view the fourth dimension could never be a physical structure that would enable us to pass through physical space, defying time but he ventured.

If the fourth dimension were to exist, it could be the place the soul seeks at the time of our death. Emotions created within us by physical activity, thinking, using our imagination, forming abstract thoughts and awareness, that condense into the essence of our being, which feeds and nourishes the soul whilst we are alive.

At the time of our death, the soul finds the fourth dimension, the link between physical life and life after death. It is the fourth dimension that transports the soul to God and its place of origin. Could this really be possible?

I sat reading, not sure what to expect next, I needed a break so I went and made some coffee, I asked Len if he wanted a coffee, no answer, I looked over, he was hunched over his computer, locked in thought another world away, where coffee didn't exist, I made a point of not disturbing him when he was like this, it was if he was in a trance. Instead, I made my way to the kitchen and made my drink and sat looking out over the desert towards the pyramids, thirty minutes later, refreshed I went back to the living room and continued reading.

No matter how hard we try to quantify the feelings within us during our lives, there are no calculations as such which determine exactly how complex the problem might be and where the fourth dimension might reside, within us, in or outside of the Universe, if the fourth dimension is real or has any significance. This type of feeling, that there are no boundaries to our life or the Universe, comes and goes during our lives. Within all of us there is a yearning, a belief that we don't just die as part of natural evolution, that there must be more to our being than our physical bodies we walk around in. No matter what Charles Darwin's theory of evolution or science suggests, the great civilisation which was Egypt from 5,000 BC to 150 AD the birth of Jesus Christ, are the clearest signs that there is life after death.

Len's conclusion was that the fourth dimension is the route by which the soul is transported back from where it came, he had written:

There is within all of us 'a certain something which, makes us question 'who are we, where did we come from and where are we going' and to ask, is this all there is to life? Are we to accept that after three score years and ten, we die; we are no more other than the dust that blows in the wind? From the concepts of two and 3-dimensional space, analysis using complex calculations, telescopes, spectrograms and the like, scientists confidently suggest that there is a fourth dimension, in the same way that they tell us the Universe is trillions of light-years in size, something like 13.5 billion years old and the Earth was formed around 4 billion years ago from a ball of dust and gas discharged from the sun.

In pursuit of the fourth dimension, who would really dare to visit the coldest places in space where the temperature is defined as zero, so cold that physical movement and life ceases to exist and has been given the mathematical number of minus 273 Celsius to its temperature.

Trying to evaluate and quantify the streams of abstract data that there is life after death, is a leap of faith often too far for the scientific mind, the constraints of A x B x C are too small and limiting, a different approach is needed to complete the calculation in non-scientific terms. If a calculation were possible, it might be defined as 'the amount of goodness x love x compassion' which equals 'nourishment of the soul' and subsequent access to the fourth dimension where God, the Supreme Being resides when we depart our physical bodies. But how could we possibly measure or prove that? 'The book of the dead' discovered by E A Wallis Budge in 1888 provides some clues, Budge was a prolific writer and better for being known.

Even if we could set up the calculation, would we ever know or be certain that we had done enough to progress to the fourth dimension or to use a non-scientific calculation, if we had not done enough or had not been true to ourselves, then at the time of our death, we pass into a 'black hole' crushed and cast into darkness and oblivion for eternity or as depicted in the 'book of the dead' if the heart weighs more than the feather of truth, we are consumed by Ammut. Science and Darwinism indicate the calculations depicted in the 'Book of the dead, are not possible but this is the only calculation that has any worth; 'if' you believe as the Egyptians did, in eternal life: that the essence of our being resides in our soul, our 'absolute thoughts' and the things we create, made from them, are the 'ingredients' of the calculation.

I put Len's notes down on the table, relieved in a way. For a moment I thought Len had joined the band of scientists that actually believe in a physical fourth dimension.

I looked over; Len seemed to have hardly moved other than his fingers as they tapped gently over the keyboard. He must have been reading my thoughts for his head turned slowly, a small smile on his face, I thought he was going to say something, instead he returned to face the computer screen, it wasn't cold in the living room but the silence made me think, it must be similar to outer space.

Seventeen

Giza, Egypt April 2012

I re-read Len's words over again, it made me realise that the study of science and mathematics must be a very cold and lonely existence. His words chilled me to the bone. It was for these pursuits, that Len's life was to come to a sudden and dramatic end, about a month after he had died, I found a few more notes relating to the fourth dimension, he had written:

There is no warmth in reason and logic, just bunches of calculations, piles of prime and pure numbers continually replacing each other in the pursuit of mathematical absolutes. There is beauty in the mathematics but it is a cold, isolated beauty shared only by a small group of mathematicians, mainly geniuses of course but they are unable to share the rare beauty of numbers with ordinary people. The irony being the one 'absolute' which is essential to human wellness, that brings colour and purpose to life. Love is absent by sciences own rigid logic and has no number. Passion the mixture of irrepressible and unstable thoughts and ideas will always distort mathematical calculations.

The following sentence was written in red and underlined.

Something the true scientist must never allow. For the mathematician, there are no random numbers (not even zero) every number on its own, as a prime, transcendental or in any combination are beautiful and pure. They are the canon of reason for some they are God; numbers are the creators of everything known only to mankind.

Eighteen

Giza, Egypt April 2012

The questions and the continued search to find the missing link between natural evolution and creationism brought me to trying to make sense of Len's last notes, which embraced Savants/Savant Syndrome and Synaesthesia. Whilst we agreed that Darwin and Wallace had identified mankind's place in the evolutionary tree that made perfect scientific sense and difficult to dismiss, there was a nagging doubt that this was the complete story of how mankind evolved. Len had already suggested the magnificent buildings, temples, the great pyramid of Giza and the artefacts left by the Egyptian Empire seemed far removed and different from any other nation of peoples evolving at the same time 4,500 years ago.

I was on firmer ground researching Savants and their unique abilities than trying to keep us with Len's theories on mathematics and the value of zero. For me, there had always been an endless fascination with the Egyptian Empire and their way of life six thousand years ago. An example of the complexity and beauty of their wisdom and ritual is illustrated on a Papyrus dated 1,375 BC which depicts a scene of Honefer's heart being weighed against the feather of truth: officiated by Anubis the Jackal headed judge, also known as 'the God of the Dead' with the Ibis headed scribe also known as 'The God of wisdom' in attendance, recording the result of the trial. I referred back to Len's notes, he had written:

From 2,500 BC the Egyptians believed access to the afterlife depended on the deceased heart weighing less than the feather of truth, success leads to the deceased soul being presented to Osiris. Where the heart weighed more than the feather of truth the unfortunate candidate awaiting progress to the afterlife was eaten by a waiting Chimie devouring creature having the head of a crocodile, the forelegs of a lion and the rear of a hippopotamus, known as Ammut.

Like everything Egyptian, the papyrus describing the scene has beautiful colour, symbolism and symmetry. A timeless quality which when viewed today seems as fresh and relevant as it was then 3386 years ago. I wondered, where the animal-headed beings depicted in 'The book of the dead' had come from. Were they symbols of an ancient religion, pageantry around a story of religious belief or could it be that God had actually created these half animal half human beings alongside mankind. Anubis, the Jackal headed judge, Ibis the bird-headed scribe and the complex three-part creature Ammut might have been demi-gods from another world or simply living creatures or a figment of the imagination.

Len thought Egyptians were too knowledgeable, serious and respectful to be fanciful to have made up God's, he had written:

These strange headed beings may not have been around during the period covering the Egyptian Empire from 5,000 BC to 1,500 BC but they could have been part of everyday life in a pre-Egyptian, Atlantis. The records of what these Gods looked like and the rituals they performed for those passing into the afterlife handed down from the Atlantians to the Egyptians.

The book of the Dead' challenges our modern concepts of life and death and speaks of the netherworld. A way of understanding the complexity of Egyptian life, the courts and palaces of the Pharaohs, their religion and beliefs there is no better book than Christine Desroches Noble-Courts comprehensive and beautifully illustrated book 'Tutankhamen'.

It's worth remembering that at the height of this great civilisation 4,500 BC the life of people in Europe and Britain was very different, illustrated by the remains of a small settlement found at Skara Brea in the Orkneys, comprising around twenty small stone-built houses with simple furniture, a long way short of the civilisation and architecture of Egypt.

Equally, we must not forget that Stonehenge was built at approximately the same time as the Great Pyramid of Cheops, another time machine but not in my opinion on the scale of Cheops.

The civilisations of India and Sumeria are said to be equally old and sophisticated as those of Egypt 5,000 years ago, this may be so but it is the Egyptian Empire with all its mystery, majesty and remaining artefacts that captures the imagination and leads so many people from every country in the world to spend their lives immersed in its study.

1375 years after the reign of Tutankhamen, a major event took place.

The birth of Jesus Christ who it was claimed was the son of God, very much in human form, re-affirmed to those who doubted, that mankind was indeed created by God, the Supreme Being.

These claims have over a period of 2,000 years extended to every corner of the world where Christianity in many denominations is practiced by over a billion people and the belief in God and an afterlife remains as strong now in some countries as it did then. Equally other mainstream religions including Buddhists, Hindus, Jews, Mormons, Muslims and Seiks believe in life after death.

Sadly in many developed westernised countries, spiritual belief is on the wane, being replaced by physical pleasure materialism and greed, in a word hedonism.

Today, unwanted children can be aborted as easily as moving house and quicker, changing a job, the childless mother returns to work the next day. Another example of how strange and negative some 'absolute thoughts' have become is how so many people worry endlessly about their looks, size and shape of their bodies, or damage them with drugs and self-harm, if they don't come up to their own expectations.

Perhaps we have evolved too far? I don't think people in our material world are really happy. The link with spiritual life is fast vanishing as we replace one form of material wealth and wellbeing with another. Ammut the three-part creature depicted in the book of the dead, hungrily looks on, the stagnant smell of waste and dead people that are still alive, pervades the air as they pursue their empty lives. Gauguin's famous painting silently echoes a warning "D'Ou Venons nous? Que Sommes Nous? Qu Allons Nous?" Where do we come from? What are we? Where are we going? But how many of us see or hear?

Len was is in a black mood as we doubled back over his research, looking for other groups of people who would have been around at the time of the Egyptian empire, whose way of life was the same then as it is today. Len's mood lightens as we find contradictions and anomalies in human development.

The Ayoreo Indians of Paraguay, the Nukak Indians of Colombia along with other remote tribes of people living in Brazil, Papua New Guinea, Peru, Bolivia and many other tribes of people, live very much in the same way as they did some 6,000 years or so ago. You would expect them to have developed much more than they have to support Darwin and Wallace's theory of mankind's natural evolution. I recorded the following from Len's notes.

It was clear to me that the Egyptian civilisation of 6,000 years ago and that of the Maya peoples in Mexico of the same time do not fit quite as easily into the Darwin theories alongside the native tribes of the time, who today are still living a very basic and nomadic way of life. What made the Egyptians and Maya people so different from the

Ayoreo, and Nukak Indians?

Not natural evolution, the more I think about it the more I feel the Egyptian Civilisation does not fit into Darwin's evolutionary tree at all. I wondered why both the Egyptian and Maya civilisations had disappeared so suddenly and why the following generations had been unable to build on their legacies. Today both countries are a shadow of their former glory, the brilliance and fame linked intrinsically to their past has gone, with nothing new to offer. They were the greatest civilisation known to man and still remain a mystery, as if locked in a time bubble, their brilliant past captured so clearly in their understanding of mathematics, astronomy, architecture, metalwork and furniture. We must not forget the beautiful hieroglyphs, paintings on papyrus and murals never repeated by later civilisations. The secrets of their knowledge locked in the ancient tombs of Tutankhamen, the Great Pyramid of Cheops and the vaults below the Sphinx, for thousands of years these monuments have laid dormant but their beauty remains and is timeless, evoking within us an aching to return to the lost world.

For all our current knowledge of the ancient world, these monuments defy scientific understanding and spiritual interpretation.

The Mortuary Temple buildings of Mentuhosep in Luxor and Hatshepsut in Upper Egypt look so modern and elegant, if you didn't know their age you might think it could have been designed by Frank Lloyd Wright or Corbusier.

Today, Architects and Structural Engineers have speculated on how these enormous structures might have been built with the use of sanded ramps, wooden rollers, ropes and thousands of men in their construction but these findings even if true, do nothing to explain the why of it.

In the Engineers mind the use of ropes and wooden rollers, the mass of labour dumb-down these wondrous buildings, bringing them into a human scale, something they can relate too and begin to understand. The suggestion follows that these great temples and monuments weren't inspired or built by Gods after all but simply by ingenious techniques and human endeavour I believe misses the point.

Like 'absolute thought' which they are, these great monuments were un-necessary in maintaining everyday life in the Nile Valley; After many years of research, I believe their purpose was divine and Godly! The visionary Architects that created these buildings, like the disciples named in the bible Mathew, Mark, Luke and John who followed them, they were high priests, God's message created in monuments, carved in stone.

Whilst our Architects and Engineers debate the construction of these buildings it is interesting to note that many of our twentieth-century buildings are constructed with steel or concrete frames supporting the external walls panels, floors and roof.

It is known that both concrete and steel lose their load-bearing capacities after a nominal period of time and the life of our modern-day monuments might be as little as 200 to 300 years before they are considered unsafe and have to be demolished, whilst the Great pyramid of Giza built some 4,500 years ago, remains as do many other monuments thousands of years old, this in itself should tell us something about mankind's progress. Interestingly Ignatius Donnelly suggested in his book of the Great Pyramid that the Great Pyramid was the first pyramid to be built and the rest including the stepped pyramids were merely later attempts to recreate the pyramid. The obvious scientific thought being that the step pyramids were the first and the great pyramid the last an example of man's building evolution.

Nineteen

Giza Egypt April 2012

In those final days, although Len looked ill, he didn't look like he was about to die, if anything he had more about him, I was genuinely pleased for him and myself. I felt a little more relaxed and hopeful that we would complete his work.

We found ourselves reading more and more books as part of our research that took us along a new path to establish/confirm either Charles Darwin's theory of natural evolution or God's creationism.

The most compelling books being John Michelle's, View over Atlantis, along with David Furlong's, The Keys to the Temple, keenly followed by Alfred Watkins, The Old Straight Track.

John Michelle describes an Atlantian world, linking the pyramids of Giza to Stonehenge Silsbury pieced together with historical artefacts, sacred geometry and numerology, bursting with the insight and passion of a true believer of Atlantis, a lost world the foundation of the civilisation. Michelle's findings underpinned and strengthened by David Furlongs equally impressive books pushed Len's leanings towards creationism. David Furlongs, 'The Keys to the Temple' identifies two massive circles of twelve-mile diameter, interlinked that pick up sacred sites in England in addition to Watkins 'Ley Lines' he shows the circles as having a link with the Great Pyramid.

CW Ceram's Gods, Graves and Scholars, was another

writer that provided a tenuous link to the mystery facing us but in a different way. What was striking in Ceram's book was the reference to the number of Autodidactics who had devoted their lives to researching ancient civilisations, asking the same historical questions posed over the centuries and now in our modest way by Len and myself.

Len ended up, identifying five groups, people that he considered represented the pinnacle of human achievement, relating to 'intelligence' and 'abstract thought', gifted people who didn't fit into the theory of natural evolution as neatly as Darwinists would like, Len had written some notes for each group:

First, there were autodidactic's, people who were self-taught to a very high standard. There is nothing to say these people don't fit into the pattern of mankind's development of natural evolution but when we consider autodidactic's such as the multilingual Jean-Francois Champollion, or ironically Alfred Wallace who did not have the benefit of Darwin's education, both mainly self-taught, we found ourselves thinking more carefully, how did they acquire their knowledge.

The Autodidactics unique ability of acquiring knowledge on their own in a non-conventional way covers every field of human activity. Cutting through the structures of academic-based learning they acquire knowledge, as if the structures didn't exist.

I think of them as enigmas, Heston Blumenthal the internationally renowned chef is a modern-day example of a self-taught autodidactic, the story goes that having taught himself how to cook English dishes from a young age. Heston purchased an English/French dictionary so that he could understand and learn French recipes that he then proceeded to cook to the highest standards. Not only is he a great chef but he brought a unique science to the kitchen a unique way of preparing food, he has made it possible for any would-be aspiring cook to know they can reach the top without formal training.

Secondly, there are Prodigies, young people, especially children who have talent and knowledge of a very high standard sometimes at a very young age. Mozart comes to mind as being the most widely known prodigy.

We must not forget Shakuntala Devi India's most famous Mathematics prodigy who with no formal education, was able to complete the most complex of mathematical questions put to her in seconds, the most notable being able to multiply two thirteen digit numbers together in half a minute.

Like Autodidactics, Prodigies achievements cover most areas of human activity but are often found in music and mathematics, Carl Friedrich Gauss born in 1777, described as the Prince of Mathematicians, he was said to have been an Autodidactic and Prodigy and later as his life developed was considered a Genius. It made me think, who put the gene in the genius?

Thirdly there were polymaths, people who are proficient and learned in many subjects, the most noted polymaths are considered to be Leonardo Da Vinci and Isaac Newton along with Gauss whose achievements covered many subjects including mathematics, geometry, astronomy and optics who also falls into this category.

The fourth group, perhaps the most widely and most understood, the genesis of our world, a title bestowed on the few by the many, who marvel at their brilliance. We use science or our lack of understanding of science to identify people we believe are geneses, in reality, their status as geneses stands alone, qualification is unnecessary. Often we relate to their brilliance simply by association, in the presence of a genius, we feel good for them and also ourselves perhaps for recognising their genius. Not a bad thing if you are lucky enough to come into contact with one.

Biographies, the film and record industry and television have brought the genius into our lives where we can begin to understand

and appreciate their unique abilities, geniuses are present in every field of human endeavour.

The television brings them into our homes, the great musicians, singers, actors, sportsmen being the most enjoyed, our heroes on display, to marvel at, record for posterity and replay at will.

The fifth and final group and less well-known, being Savant, people who have unique abilities in a very narrow field of activity. There is no current explanation for their unique abilities, though there is intense interest and research taking place to try and unlock the secrets to their ability. It can also be said that because they acquire their abilities themselves, they are also autodidacts by definition; equally many Savants are able to demonstrate their unique abilities from an early age so could be classed as Prodigies as well. The most widely known Savants today are Kim Peek, Daniel Trammet and Steven Bishop.

These five groups of people are very rare in size of world population; their numbers and categories can never properly qualify or quantify them, as hard as statisticians might try.

Singularly and together they pose a fundamental question, how do these gifted people acquire their knowledge, importantly is it simply genetically evolved as part of the evolutionary process or is it God-given?

Four people all Archaeologists stand out in Ceram's book, they could all be described as 'Autodidactics'. Their single-minded pursuit of historical facts and archaeological sites stand today, as remarkable achievements.

These great men share a unique place in history. Henrich Schliemann was born in

1822; at the age of eight he had a vision that one day he would discover the City of

Troy. A brilliant linguist, Henrich Schliemann spoke 13

different languages, many

acquired from childhood. Some fifty years later his boyhood dream became reality.

There has been a lot of criticism relating to Schliemann's methods of excavating

archaeological sites but it could also be said that, without his vision and tireless

endeavour however crude, the city of Troy would have remained undiscovered.

Henrich led a full life; he made a fortune in America as a young man before

travelling to Greece to begin his quest to un-earth Troy.

He died on Boxing Day 1890; he was buried fittingly in the first cemetery of Athens

and his home was turned into a museum known as the Numismatic Museum of Athens.

Jean-Francois Champollion a Frenchman was born in 1790 and became famous for unravelling the mysteries of Egyptian Hieroglyphics. As a child he too had an unusual grasp of many different languages, though it is said, he never attended school, Jacques his older brother taught him to read, by the age of 20 Jean had mastered 13 languages and had begun to learn then study the ancient Coptic language which was to provide the link to solving the mystery of Egyptian Hieroglyphics, his translation was first published in 1822, ten years later at the age of 41, this great man died in the prime of life, a huge loss to science and Egyptology.

Claudius James Rich was also born in France but to British parents in 1787 was another young man who had a gift for languages from a very early age. He was also self-taught His talent for languages lent themselves to his investigations of the history and geography of Babylon, then later Basra and Shiraz in what was then known as Persia. Much of his work is set out in 'Narrative of a Journey to the site of Babylon' 1811 and 'Narrative of a residence in Koordistan'. Sadly Claudius died at the age of 34 from cholera. To make up the quartet of brilliant Autodidactics we have to include William Matthew Flinders Petrie born in 1853, described by his peers as one of the foremost Egyptologists and another hero of mine.

Like Champollion, Petrie was educated at home, receiving no formal education. He was encouraged by his father to take an interest in archaeology. His father also taught him how to survey land and ancient monuments.

Along with Howard Carter one of his protégées, Petrie was acknowledged as one of the leading and subsequently the most famous Egyptologists, his most important discovery being that of Merneptah Stele, Petrie died in Jerusalem in 1942 where he was buried.

These men, self-taught and proficient in many languages, acquired from childhood could also it into the other categories, Prodigies, Polymaths, Genius or Savants? Their talent seemingly overlapping from one category to another. In any event, their thirst for knowledge of ancient civilisations was underpinned by tireless dedication and an attention to detail.

Ceram identified other autodidacts, whose pursuit and studies of science changed the face of the world. Perhaps the most well-known and famous being Michael Faraday (1791-1867) born in London, he had only a basic formal education and began his working life as a bookbinder.

Self-taught he went on to become a chemist and contributed to the understanding of electromagnetism and electrochemistry.

There was also Herbert G Wells, another hero of mine; very much self-taught who captured the imaginations of people worldwide with his books on science fiction. Alongside Schliemann, Champollion, Rich and Petrie, Ceram's account of how these great men work, suggested to me that the base of their knowledge was innate in content, brought into being and developed by a visionary quest to find and understand ancient religions, the way of life and artefacts of the great civilisations of the past.

If some areas of knowledge are innate rather than acquired as we grow up, where does innate knowledge come from? We know intellect and behaviour are located in our DNA, passing through generations, evolving through natural evolution?

But why were these five groups of people so different from the rest of mankind? That was the question I kept asking myself.

Sometimes if it was warm enough we would sit on the balcony, watching the sun rise from behind the great pyramid, the first rays of sunlight illuminating the outline of the pyramid, giving the appearance that it was alive, glowing, pulsating with energy as it seemed to rise out of the ground, the effect for the short time it lasted was magical. Len would sit with his knees tucked up under his chin, his Oxford blue scarf covering most of his face hung down around his dressing gown and a blanket to hand. I was usually fully dressed, when it was chilly I would wear the full-length calfskin coat my father had given me. We didn't talk much, both of us sitting silently in worlds of our own.

One particular day sitting alone in Len's flat, I found myself thoroughly stuck in the analysis and meanings of words. This was one of the major problems I had writing Len's notes. How to be both specific and be able to generalise at the same time. I began to realise unless I was very careful, it was so easy for the words written to have a different meaning to that intended. I also began to realise that as soon as I resolved one issue, another came along. These thoughts crossed my mind as I sat on the balcony.

I felt incredibly alone; looking over at Len who had just

come in, having been for a walk, I sensed he had the same feelings as me but probably for different reasons.

Why me? Why had I chosen to get involved in writing a thesis on such complex issues? Once the sun had moved above the baseline of the Pyramid the change in temperature became quickly noticeable, Len pulled his scarf from around his face, turned towards me and smiled his weak smile, I still hoped for the best, though Len looked very pale, but I could never have imagined that in a few days' time he would be dead, he still seemed eager to push on.

"Len, we need to clarify our thoughts on 'geniuses' and include something on IQ tests." Len agreed, by now the temperature was rising fast; we went inside where it was cooler and had some breakfast before we started another day discussing and researching Len's ideas, I made some notes as Len expounded his theory.

"The term genius sits easily beside prodigy and autodidactic in the right context. To my mind, all these gifted people have much in common. To separate the difference between say genius and a savant can only be attempted crudely, perhaps by their numbers, in that there are more geniuses in the world at any one time than Savants and their work in most cases can be better understood and used than Savants. In any event, geniuses are a very rare group of people with exceptional talent, ability craftsmanship and originality.

Anders Ericsson calibrated that it took approximately 10,000 hours, approximately 5 years for someone totally dedicated to the subject of his interest, to completely master it as a way of describing a genius. Frankly, I don't buy this; it demeans the meaning of genius.

Mozart followed by Mendelssohn put Ericsson's observations into perspective when as very young children they were not only proficient in playing musical instruments but by the age of seven, both were composing music. What were these brilliant young men trying to convey?

Today most people agree that music, in all its forms from classical to popular music, speaks directly to the soul, impassioning and transporting us into another world of dreams and eternal life, for a short time music replaces the mundaneness of everyday life.

Art can have a similar effect, as does poetry and writing, but in the main, it is music, theatre, ballet, opera and film, running parallel to real life, that transports us into a surreal world which confirms to me there is more to our lives than the routine behaviour of merely existing and the scientists endless analysis of matter that when defined tell us, we are no more than dust, when we die, something Len and I could never except."

Thinking back, on a different wavelength the Child prodigy, Bernard Riemann whose grasp of complex mathematics, reminded me of how fragile brilliance can be. Riemann like Len had a fragile mind and suffered several mental breakdowns but, unlike Len, he was able to overcome his fears and shyness and become a brilliant and renowned mathematician.

On a scrap of paper Len had written:

I can imagine that everyone of great intelligence and ability at some time or another fears for their sanity, in a way their brilliance must isolate them from society.

Len's prophetic words made me smile; he had described himself to a tee, though he didn't see himself as being anything out of the ordinary that was one of the things I really liked about Len.

Returning to the thesis, we agreed that to properly understand the mind and abilities of a Genius or Savant you would have to be one.

Myself, no-way, I was just your normal American Indian trying to get a life, my greatest achievement until I met Len was riding king down the mother road, travelling over 100 miles an hour, perhaps it was fate that I happened to meet Leonard Balthazar, who to my mind was a genius and probably a savant.

Words alone can never describe his phenomenal abilities in a way other people might understand, a bit like the big numbers that Scientists so love, I read on.

A person's intelligence quota better known as their IQ is used by Organisations, Teachers, Doctors and people in the academic world to gauge someone's intellect, their ability to learn and problem solve. In addition to identifying an individual's ability, IQ tests are also used to assess the general level of nation ability and then the full spectrum of people in the world. The scale of ability is measured from 0 to 150 and has been identified by those setting the tests that 98% of people fall between 75 and 120. The genius's scaling 148 or over being in the last 2 per cent of people tested, if the tests tell us anything it is that the level of intelligence required to live our lives successfully is between 75 to 120, though there are not two geniuses in every one hundred people it might be more like 1 in 2 million or 5 million, not a number which can be properly quantified and other than to show how rare genius' are. The IQ test has no value or meaning for measuring the genius, you can tag a person's perceived ability but not their spirit.

Put another way by Arthur Schopenhauer who is quoted as saying, Talent hits a target no one else can hit, Genius hits a target no one else can see.

I smiled,

"I like that, Len, it's so neat."

Laughing we both agreed with Schopenhauer's thoughts on geniuses, coming to the conclusion that humans are too preoccupied with measuring; intelligence is another example of our fascination with abstract thought. In a roundabout way, 'abstract thought' highlights the weakness of Darwinism, the science that sets out to chronicle and measure every living object that can be measured. The inexplicable, the para-normal are given a different measure and definition that fits within the limits of science and understanding or is quietly discarded, I leafed through Len's notes.

The academic is unlikely to jump out of the box and look within; not always, but mostly lateral thinking is rarely part of their make up.

At heart, the Scientist is likely to be an atheist for him nothing exists that he can't see. For reaffirmation everything that can be measured is measured and re-measured time and again to erase any doubt that he might be wrong but as I have said before, in general terms a scientist doesn't measure what he can't see, therefore to him God is unlikely to exist. I do not wish to cause offence and accept that there are many scientists that do believe in God, the Supreme Being and have dedicated their lives to his work. The statement is a generalisation, perhaps I should re-phrase it to say, a scientist is unlikely to believe in a supreme being a lack of proof.

It's perhaps unfair and annoying that those who believe in life after death in 'creationism' don't have to have any prior knowledge; belief and acceptance in a 'supreme being' only requires faith, not actual proof, on the other hand, the atheist to be absolutely sure that there is no supreme being requires a considerable amount of thinking, time and knowledge, it could be said that to be absolutely sure, the atheist would need to know everything ever written or spoken before he is able to properly dismiss the presence of a supreme being.

Len's words made me smile again; it was typical of his way of reasoning when he had the bit between his teeth. He considered there was a difference between the structured behaviour bound into everyone's DNA which is the make up of mankind and essential to procreation and our daily survival, than abstract knowledge, making us so much more complex than we need just to survive.

For example, our ability to speak multiple languages or indulge in pure mathematics from childhood, which have only limited and specific use. Why are we 'human beings' so wrapped up in contemplation and absorbed with abstract thought? Perhaps this is our legacy and own immortality when we die?

By contrast and to illustrate the opposing point of view, Len had written:

Darwinist's can take comfort from the skeleton of 'Cheddar Man' found at the entrance of a cave in Somerset around 1900, thought to be between 7,000 to 9,000 years old. Thanks to the work of Bryan Sykes the skeleton of Cheddar Man has been carbon-dated and incredibly Cheddar Man's DNA has been matched to people living today in England. This is defiantly one up for the Darwin camp.

Finishing off Len's notes I noticed he had scribbled in the margins of the paper.

The atheist would champion this evidence; on its own, it's enough to put the God created hocus-pocus to bed once and for all.

When we discussed 'Cheddar Man' we agreed this compelling evidence cannot be dismissed in scientific terms, but like millions of people living today who believe that there is a God and life after death, neither of us were convinced by the discovery of 'Cheddar man' or Darwin's theory of natural evolution as to how mankind evolved.

For Len there was still an inexplicable question in his mind that would not go away? Perhaps it was the thought that whilst Cheddar Man resided in his caves for shelter, hunting and living mainly on horse meat, the great civilisations in the Middle East were evolving in spectacular fashion, I referred back to his notes.

I am fascinated and inspired by the backgrounds of Schliemann, Chamopllion, Rich and Petire, just four of the many great men inspired and driven by a need to research the past, spending their lives unlocking the secrets of the distant past.

Len firmly believed that anyone of a certain disposition would be drawn into the world of Egyptology if they set eyes on this magical land or from a distance are captured by the paintings and spells portrayed in 'the book of the dead', or seeing for the first time the fabulous contents of Tutankhamen's Tomb, the Great Pyramid, the iconic Sphinx whose edifying gaze stretches across the desert sand, passing through time through one millennium to another. Len had summed it up succinctly, saying.

"Who couldn't fail to be moved and inspired by these great men and the wondrous artefacts of the past?"

Our attention was drawn further towards people given the labels, Autodidacts, Polymaths, Prodigies and Geniuses mainly whose self-taught abilities run in front of structured learning, as if some form of innate knowledge drives their psyche and purpose in life and then on to modern-day Savants such as Daniel Trammet, Steven Bishop and the late Kim Peek to name just three whose abilities surpass Autodidacts, Polymaths and Prodigies, can only be described as beyond normal understanding. Savants are subject to intense observation in the scientific and medical world, running alongside the study of people with Autism to which Savant Syndrome is closely linked, Len had written:

What is generally acknowledged by the Medical and Scientific communities is that Savants are able to undertake feats of memory recall and mathematical calculation effortlessly, way beyond current medical and scientific understanding.

It is thought that Savants suffer from Autism though not all Savants are Autistic. Importantly only a very small number of people suffering from Autism are Savants. Research has also identified that there are more male Savants than female and their numbers are few. From the little I understand of Savants abilities it was clear to me that, like the people of the Egyptian Civilisation 3,000 BC but in a different context, Savants don't fit neatly into the Darwinian theory of evolution.

Len said there must be another answer I referred to his notes, he had written:

The critical issue being were Savants born with their remarkable inherent abilities or were their abilities developed or triggered from an illness (Autism) or other rare circumstances in early childhood. In any event, the resultant examples of their brilliance stand alone in human achievement and are the unmeasurable defying explanation.

Professor Christopher Wills in his book 'The Runaway Brain.' identifies that the DNA structure which links humans to the chimpanzee reinforces Darwin's theory of evolution, underpinned by the skeleton of 'Cheddar man' but my instinct is that the overwhelming scientific data assembled on the Darwin side of the debate, does not address the question of how, for example: a small number of 'Savants' come to be living in the same world as ourselves. Darold Treffert the eminent doctor and leading authority on Autism and Savant's suggest there might be 50 Savant's currently alive).

Savants feature only briefly in 'Wills' book. Surprisingly Wills does not appear overly struck by the achievements of Savants, suggesting that their narrow field of expertise is developed mainly by hard work, practice and their ability to focus on one subject at the expense of all others.

I begged to differ. When I read for example, that by the age of seven Kim Peek's had read and memorised the Bible, followed up by reading and memorising the complete works of Shakespeare made me sit up and take notice.

Will's conclusions were that Savants ability resides mainly on their ability to practice their chosen subject.

"No way," Len had said.

"It just doesn't stack up. In his glossary of terms, Will's refers to Savants as being people with mental retardation who none the less can develop particular skills to a high level. I was profoundly disappointed with this summary of Savants; in no way does Professor Wills a talented writer begin to understand Savants super-human powers."

Coming to the end of this area of research. Len shrugging his shoulders and had written:

It was a classic example of the scientific mindset, being able to only analyse what is on the table and capable of being analysed, adding that unless they are able to repeat any of the stupendous feats that Savants undertake on a routine basis, Scientists and Academics are not really in a position to do otherwise than observe the phenomenal power of a Savants mind'.

Instead of accepting Will's observations on Savants it only reinforced Len's intense belief that there was a missing link in Charles Darwin's theory, prompting him to investigate further but then his research took another direction returning to the monuments and signposts of religious belief. The portals of evidence left by the distant civilisations of mankind.

Len came to several conclusions, mainly that Alfred Watkins 'ley lines' a term Watkins used in 'The Old Straight Track' published in 1925 to describe tracts linking several sacred land marks over parts of southern England pointed to Jon Michelle being right in linking Atlantis with the sacred geometry of the Great Pyramid of Giza, Stonehenge, Salisbury in England, we felt that in some way 'ley lines' were an integral part of solving the mystery.

What was inspiring about Michelle's book, 'The view over Atlantis' was that it was breathtaking, as were his insights into a forgotten world?

The complex research and detail supporting Michelle's ideas wrapped in a kind of prose which harkened back to William Blake but at the same time, there was nothing pompous or self-serving about Michelle.

He was Len said, another dedicated pioneer in search of ancient wisdom, driven with the notion that mankind had in essence, lost its spiritual way of life and the key to developing a more fulfilled life lay in understanding the civilisations of the past, when mankind connected fully with his spiritual self.

The pages of Michelle's book and equally those of David Furlong and Eric Von Daniken tell of an Ancient knowledge which was superior to our own.

Eric Von Daniken's book 'Chariots of the Gods' spreads the net of mysterious objects, artefacts and fantastic ruins scattered all over the world was somewhat spoilt, by on his own admission, that some of the facts claimed could not be properly supported, bringing his credibility and that of the subject into dispute.

Whatever the misgivings of Daniken's admitted misjudgements, he was articulate and wrote with passion and whatever the conjecture surrounding his books, the evidence is still there, enough we thought to challenge the sceptics who said Daniken's claims that Aliens visited the Earth were pseudoscience.

A term Len said could be equally applied too many

scientific claims, in particular the big bang theory, the expanding Universe and the concept of absolute zero.

Writing up the last of Len's notes made me recall one evening when Len had momentarily stopped chasing Rienmann's elusive zeros, we were sitting on the balcony drinking mint tea. It was shortly before his brain haemorrhage; for once he seemed happy and relaxed.

"Just as the sceptics had hammered down Von Daniken, believing they had re-established the status quo other pioneers seeking the truth come along."

Len was laughing as he spoke.

"When do you get time to read all this stuff, Len?"

I was genuinely interested; I had never seen him with a book of.

"You know Henry, I don't sleep, I catch up with my reading in the early hours."

He paused taking a sip of tea, then added. *"After Daniken, there was Temple with his books on Sirius, this blew up a storm and then later Lynn Pickett and Clive Prince with their book 'The Star-gate Conspiracy' well researched and more convincing, frightening to think Governments around the world spend so much time tracking aliens real or imagined."*

Leaning over the balcony pointing towards the sphinx, Len said.

"No matter how high the sceptics build their dams to withstand the presence of a 'Supreme Being' plugging the holes with the building blocks of natural evolution, the big bang, the expanding Universe and Darwin's natural evolution, bit by bit the dam will crack and then burst, the truth of mankind's inheritance will become universally accepted."

There was a strange look on Len's face; his face was

contorting, he looked as if he was dividing himself in two, questioning and trying to balance his beliefs against his rational as they unfolded and what it would mean to him and fellow academics if he was right? I listened intently.

"Some aspects of science as we know it and recorded history Henry will have to be reassessed but the truth will find its own way to flow into the open, where it can be seen. Until now it has remained mainly hidden but truth does not die, truth endures and flows through time whether seen or unseen."

Len turned around facing me and went back to his chair, he was sweating and looked dishevelled, pushing his hands through his hair he sat down. *"Sorry, Henry I am banging on a bit."*

"Nothing to be sorry for Len, you've struck a chord, I couldn't begin to do what you do, I admire your passion and the energy you throw at it, I just write the notes."

Though I was concerned, I smiled, the sun had disappeared over the horizon and it had suddenly got cold. We returned to the sitting room. Len's mood was changing again, he was firing up, I guessed it was going to be a long night.

Back inside Len took up where he had left off.

"If as Michelle, Furlong and Von Daniken suggest that Gods visited the Earth sometime before the Egyptian civilisation creating Atlantis, where they settled, and then when Atlantis was destroyed, it's not unreasonable to assume that the Egyptian civilisation was either a colony or development of the remnants of Atlantis."

These thoughts led us back to Watkins and his 'Ley lines' and David Furlongs circles and to find an answer for what they depicted. What was their significance, what were the 'Lye lines and Circles' trying to tell us?

He came up with a theory that the specific points along Watkins 'Ley lines' and Furlongs 12-mile diameter circles, could have been the places, markers where space ships had landed perhaps from Atlantis or somewhere else in the Universe, in the case of Stonehenge the location where the solstice can be perfectly witnessed each year. Later to become the sacred sites over which the peoples of England, Peru and Egypt built their monuments.

The mathematical accuracy between the various sites telling us that they were not defined by man but by a 'supreme being' or his winged messengers, linking the sites through mathematics to the great pyramid as David Furlong has surmised, a message of conformation that mankind is part of God's creation and not natural evolution.

The Egyptian and Greek legends along with many other manuscripts, speak of God/Gods created/visited and inhabited the Earth and in some accounts suggest they interbred with the people of the land, hence it followed that those who claimed to be the direct descendants of the Gods were named as Pharaohs in Egypt the Kings and Queens of their nation. If this were true, it suggested another missing link that we were looking for. Jesus Christ called himself the 'Son of God' reaffirming the truth of God as the Supreme Being.

The followers of Jesus described as Christians cover a period of some 2,000 years, Christians practice their belief in every corner of the world, this does not necessarily make the claims of creationism 'a given', but it confirms that many millions of people think along these lines despite the science, of natural evolution.

For many in the Western world, Jesus Christ is the defining person who leads the way to the belief in life after death and underwrites the claim that God created the world and mankind in six days.

Len's interpretation of Christopher Will's book was that there was no obvious link between mankind's natural evolution and the small unique group of people known as Savants.

This did not mean that Savants were not also ordinary human beings but when we listed the things Savants were capable of doing, we asked ourselves again, were they one of the missing links, and if their powers were superhuman, were Savants themselves superhuman? How could they live alongside the rest of us with their phenomenal powers, what makes them different? I studied the last of notes with care, he had written:

It is generally established that Savants parents or grandparents do not have the same abilities and weren't themselves Savants. So it wasn't genetic in that sense, something else must have happened within them giving rise to their unique powers.

Doctors led by the eminent Darold Treffert have spent an increasing amount of time studying Autism and Savant Syndrome and how it is caused; the general consensus of opinion is that it is most likely to be some form of genetic imbalance or mutation.

In many cases a bright healthy child suddenly becomes Autistic, as if an isolator had been switched off, changing their lives dramatically. We are reminded that not all people suffering with Autism are Savants and not all Savants are Autistic but it is likely that some form of gene mutation causes or contributes to both conditions.

The breakthrough was sudden and unexpected. Len said it was much like walking into a darkened room and switching a light on. In that instant late in the evening talking after supper, Len started writing again, coming to this conclusion.

I believe in the same way that within the genetic code where a gene is activated or mutates to cause Autism, another gene is activated or mutates to release awesome power. When witnessed the power and abilities of Savants, can easily be described as God-like or to use the often over-used American word, 'Awesome'. I was dumbfounded. Did this tiny band of people have the power and abilities enacted by the Gods gifted to those humans they had mated with, had over the centuries mostly laid dormant in generation after generation only to be released by some trigger of gene mutation resulting in what we now term as a Savant.

Len had stopped writing; he put his pen down saying.

"What other explanation was there to describe their phenomenal powers," adding, *"memory recall is only one of the Savants prestigious abilities."*

We were both intrigued and fascinated by the life of Kim Peek an American Savant born in Salt Lake City America in 1951 to Mormon parents who later in his life was described as a mega Savant. At an early age Kim was diagnosed with a brain disease and the doctors suggested they undertake a lobotomy and that Kim become institutionalised.

Luckily, Kim's loving parents declined the offer and Kim grew up at home with his parents. Like many Savants. Kim taught himself to read and by the age of seven it was said that he had read the bible and was able to recall every word from memory. This was followed by other examples of his photographic memory with Shakespeare's complete works going the same way.

To pass the time it was said that Kim would add up the numbers from telephone directories in his head, the mental arithmetic producing sums running into trillions. Kim had also been diagnosed with 'Agenesis Corpus Callosum' a rare medical condition similar to Autism. Kim's unique gifts and illness, inspired and contributed to the making of 'The Rain Man'

The film drew information on Autism and Savants from several other Autistic Savants, the role of Raymond Babbit was sympathetically acted by Dustin Hoffman with Tom Cruise playing the supporting role of Raymond's brother.

The film was acclaimed worldwide and won an Oscar for Hoffman. At the time and still today, the film strikes a chord with many people, who perhaps for the first time were presented with the opportunity to understand the world of the Autistic and marvel at the ability of Savants.

Another example of Kim's unique ability was that he was able to read two books at once one with one eye reading one book and one eye reading the other.

It is interesting to note that it is estimated that less than half the population of the world cannot read or write properly, yet this man with his rare illness could read two books simultaneously, this fact alone should tell us something and make us think?

We both thought that Kim Peek's abilities were more than a quirk of nature. We came to the conclusion that Kim's specific field of ability and those of other Savants could be described as superhuman. They defy description and the full understanding of the most eminent of neurologists, mathematicians and psychologists.

After further research Len speculated that a 'Savant's' ability went further than those of people described as either Autodidactic and Polymaths, though noting that Kim taught himself to read he could also be described as an Autodidactic and also a genius, he was all of these things though these are only words, a small way of describing someone so truly gifted.

Running parallel with Savants' are people with Synaesthesia who are said to have heightened sensory powers.

Unlike Savant Syndrome, Synaesthesia is believed to be hereditary in many cases but interestingly like Savant Syndrome can be triggered by an accident causing a knock or damage to the brain. There are said to be many forms of Synaesthesia, covering all areas of sensory perception, until recently Synaesthesia has attracted little attention but not anymore, studies are not ongoing in St Louis Synaesthesia Laboratory.

A nice take on how Synaesthesia might have evolved and its use is nicely illustrated in Michael Cordy's novel, The Colour of Death.

We recognised that in many ways we were walking in a minefield, neither of us were Doctors or Scientists; we were simply students who questioned Darwinism theory of natural evolution and the feasibility of creationism.

It had moved on from there, now Len believed there was a strong possibility that Polymaths, Autodidactics, Prodigies, Geniuses, Savants and Synaesthetes were all part of the same family of people with unique ability's, that did not completely fit the theory of Evolution. Another example of a Polymaths and autodidactic was Edward Cowell who had taught himself Persian at the age of 15.

A few years later whilst in India he provided Edward Fitzgerald an English writer with his translation into English of the Rubaiyat of Omar Khayyam. Fitzgerald then developed the translation into the western version of Omar Khayyam's great work.

Sitting in the lounge drinking coffee early one morning

Len said he could picture in his mind, a Savants DNA, as a gene code tree. Along the trunk of the tree were hundreds of branches each one fitted with a lock that opened and closed. Len thought that somewhere along the trunk of the DNA tree, into one of the branches a key is inserted and turned, unlocking and releasing a powerful source of innate power and memory recall that allows Savants to undertake their stupendous tasks, whist at the same time another key on a different branch of the genetic tree, was turning in the opposite direction, switching off, locking or disconnecting the cells which drive the brain, providing information and instructions for the body to carry out the normal functions of everyday living.

Could Len have been right?' He went on to say.

'Were Savants and those with Synaesthesia descendants of a super race that visited the earth thousands of years ago? However hard we try analysing genetic patterns or the evolution of the species as Darwin had done some 200 years ago, the medical profession is unable to fully understand, define or categorise the ability of Savants or Synaesthetes.

Although Len was desperately tired, he couldn't switch off, later that night he went back to his laptop and after logging on to Kim Peek's web site found that Kim's father Frank Peek had written a book about his son 'The Real Rain Man' following the film.

Len needed little more to convince him, as a child he had witnessed a Savant's capabilities first hand. His friend, William Masters at the age of ten had created his own phonetic language. Kim Peak perhaps the most well-known Savant confirmed to him his belief that Savants had God-like powers.

Len understood from Wills that DNA the genetic code

'the basic fabric of life' changes minutely in any significant way over thousands of years'. Modern man carries the stamp of their forefathers, evolution is a very slow process as established in the link between man and the chimpanzee but a child of a mating between 'a God or Alien and a human' would obviously have a different DNA structure.

Len came to a conclusion that perhaps a different and rare DNA code was also present in the human race, highlighted by Savants and people with Synaesthetes syndrome, a code that when unlocked triggers in some people the power and abilities of a 'God' the paternal father or mother of 7,000 years ago.

The alternative theories as recorded in the bible, Adam and Eve were the first humans created by God to inhabit the earth or that Darwin's theory of evolution was mankind ascended from the chimpanzee does little to explain the phenomena of Savants or their innate knowledge on a vast scale, no more comprehendible than the number of stars in an expanding Universe, the concept of Zero or the size of the largest prime number found to date.

Twenty

Peru, Chile and Easter Island October 2012

Coming to the end of Len's notes I realised that I wanted to visit Peru and Easter Island, I couldn't forget the fantastic voyages the Egyptians had made across the Atlantic ocean some 5,000 to 4,500 years ago to the America's as described by Thor Heyerdahl in 'The Ra Expeditions' I wanted to see for myself the reed boats, murals of bird-headed men and most of all the Moai statues close up. There was something else as well. I knew if I didn't leave Egypt soon, I might never leave, there was something utterly compelling about this mysterious and beautiful country drawing me into its wondrous past.

I rang Len's father saying I had almost finished the book but wanted to visit Peru and Easter Island, he agreed and sensing the reason for my call, wired me sufficient money to fly to Peru on an 8-day tourist package and then on to Easter Island on a flight-only trip from Santiago airport, it turned out you could only fly into Easter Island from Chile and to compound matters, there was one flight per day, so first I would have to fly from Peru to Chile, it was becoming an expensive trip, Len's father Alexander didn't seem to mind, saying I had done all the hard work and it was a pleasure to help.

I made arrangements with Rania his housekeeper to tidy and clean the apartment and handed her the keys, then I rang Len's father saying I had left the flat and would be in touch as soon as I had finished the book, about 3 weeks give or take a day or so, he wished me well and if I ran short of money, I had only to ask.

A taxi took me to Cairo airport I was sad to leave Egypt, so many memories mostly good and of course one tragic event, the day I found Len dead in the apartment. The plane flew from Cairo to Illinois and then on to Lima Airport. The small hotel was about 15 minutes from the airport and having booked in I arranged for a tour guide and taxi to show me the sites, I wanted to visit. However, I had to make do mostly with u tube videos as I spent the best part of a week feeling sick. Bedbound I still managed to get a feel for what was once a great county on a parallel with Egypt.

Weak but feeling better I managed on days six and seven of my stay to visit some of the ancient sites around Lima, despite the fog, Tired but determined to complete the adventure I flew out of Peru's Lima airport to Santiago in Chile on a cold and windy day and had to wait a day for the next plane to Easter Island. The plane landed at the Hang A Roa airport and I booked into a cheap two-star hotel. It wasn't difficult to find a guide; Martinez a local taxi driver drove me around the island. There were around 800 to a 1,000 Moai dotted around the island, they were spectacular if that's the right word, more than I could ever imagine, to me they came over as the guardians of the island's secrets. On the last day before I flew back to Chile, Martinez drove me to Ahu Te Peu where we came upon a dead Moai, I say 'dead' because his head was resting helplessly on the ground, stones strewn around him. I suspected that long ago he too had guarded this section of the island, I felt his presence, as I stood looking out to sea, I had the feeling he wanted to talk to me but I couldn't hear what he is saying. I turned to look at his face his vacant eyes stared inward across the island as I guessed they had done for many centuries. Martinez looked at me with some concern saying it was not good to wake the dead and got into the jeep, motioning me to follow. Suddenly there was a chill in the air, a storm blowing in from the Pacific Ocean that looked angry, grey and sullen, it was eerie. That night I was tired out and in bed by nine, I still felt weak, I dreamt that one of the Moai's was hovering outside the window his huge empty eyes staring at me. "Go home," he mumbled. "There's nothing for you here." The wind howled as rain began to lash the window pane. The Moai was telling me I didn't belong here, that what I was looking for had been pillaged, stolen by pirates, adventurers many ages ago. When I woke, I couldn't be sure if I had dreamt the Moai's visit or it had actually occurred.

It came to me, the Moai were there to guard the sacred ground where dead Gods once lived. I readied to leave later in the morning; I knew the importance of respecting sacred lands, we had plenty of our own back in Arizona. I flew back to Chile and on to Los Angeles and finally on to Phoenix total exhausted. I hated to admit it but the trip had been a mistake, the only thing I learned was that Easter Island was either a sacred place where Gods had once lived or the island had become a jail where the Moai were constantly on guard to keep the dark angels in-prisoned or perhaps the giants were created by the legendry dark angels, forever facing inward unable to see out, imprisoned by their masters until the end of time. I must have caught a chill with all the travelling and the fog in Peru didn't help. There were just 12 passengers on the plane mostly tourists, to my disgust I was glad I was leaving. I thought of Professor McDonald the teacher of anthropology at Cairo University who had given me such a hard time before I met Len. McDonald would have laughed himself silly had he been a witness to my ill-thought-out trip, even though McDonald had had to leave the University in disgrace for molesting one of the female students, Jenny Stubbs, who was in our class.

Twenty-one

Arizona November 2012

When I arrived back in Phoenix, I booked into a cheap hotel, slept for 24 hours then rang my father, to let him know I was back in America. Saying I would be another week or so. He was furious with me, as I suspected he would be. Then I rang Len's father saying the book was nearly complete. I was washed out and didn't return to the homestead, other than to pick up King which I had left at Lester's Garage. I rang my father again and explained that I needed to polish the book first, I had given my word. He wasn't too pleased but reluctantly agreed. I rode King back to Phoenix and booked into another cheap hotel that suited my needs. For a week I lost myself in the bustle of Phoenix city life, sitting in cafes, drinking coffee, people watching and passing the time of day, regaining my strength for the final push. One morning I found a folded scrap of paper in one of Len's books I had brought back with me, he had written:

The shadow of the fourth dimension is cast in dreams and make-believe, providing a glimpse of 'who we are, where we came from and where we are going'. In my dream state I have visited this place where, the past, present and future merge with people I have met, places I've always known and people and places I've never known. I call this place, space-time, where the shadow of the fourth dimension unfolds and life and death become entwined as one, as if an act of a Shakespearian play. I have visited this place many times; it's a beautiful world, like no other. Sometimes I daydream and try to return but it's not the same place. I walk around but in daylight it feels empty and inhospitable. I have tried reason with myself, am I going insane? which is the real me, the person I am in my dreams or the me, here and now, pinching myself, wide awake, am I the one I see in the mirror?

I held the fragile piece of paper in my hand, tears in my eyes for a long time I just sat, feeling numb. Len's words, a final poem written by my friend the mathematician, confirmed to me that for all his love and belief in logic and mathematics as having the answers to mankind's questions, his beliefs were tempered by a greater belief, that somewhere within him God resides. Len has passed on to that place he dreamed of and had found the answer to the question that some embrace and others fear, I believe he is at peace in a better place.

Fate deals in life and death impartially and I was left to wonder, why Len but not me? Mindlessly I rode King along endless empty roads, the barren landscape rushes by, the speedometer hovers around 100, a bend in the road lay ahead, I don't bother to break, instead I brush the tears from my face and adjust my goggles with my gloved hand. 'Where did I come from? Why am I here? Where am I going? King rode the bend with aplomb. The bend in the road now behind me fades into the distance, another will arrive shortly, caught in thoughts that I wanted to live but deserved to die, I had failed Len, I opened the throttle, just how much time do I have left?

I guessed one more chapter, thank God and the most important, Len's case for creationism, Savants/Savant Syndrome and Synaesthesia but before I could start, somehow my father had tracked me down to the hotel I was using as a temporary home. Perhaps someone at the homestead had seen me and reported back to him, in any event, he phoned in the morning to ask me what I was I doing. Before I could answer he said.

"Still playing at being 'Easy Rider' Red Feather? It's time you grew up." I was surprised and a little hurt by his aggressive tone, my father rarely spoke in this manner, he followed up with.

"There's urgent work to be done, I need you here at the homestead, when are you coming home?"

It would have taken too long to explain to my father that I was undertaking a task; I had given my word to Len's father about completing the book, anyway I figured he was in no mood to listen. I apologised in a half-hearted manner adding that I had business to conclude in Phoenix and would be home as soon as possible. My apology sounded hollow, in truth I wasn't sorry at all and resented his intrusion into my personal life, he didn't own me. I listened as he accepted my apology in the same tone and half-hearted manner as mine.

I could tell he resented the fact that I could walk away from the homestead as and when it suited me. Though in reality I would never do this, if I was needed I would be there, it was how he asked that was important and I objected to being spied on, if that is what it was. I knew better than to argue with my father and also this wasn't going to be the end of it. He would pick up where he left off when I returned home, I ended the call, saying.

"Father I need to finish my business in Phoenix; it will take a week or so and I will promise I will be home no later than the first week in October."

I could hear him grumbling as he rang off. I had to complete Len's notes, the final chapter, then once I was satisfied I had to get it put on to a CD and print off a hard copy. Then, when finished, I would post the completed notes to Len's father in England. What had started out as an adventure had become a real task? Some days I enjoyed the writing, but Len's death hung over me like a shadow darkening the room and my mood. What a great start to the day, I had been disrespectful to my father, I wasn't where I should be and more angry words were sure to follow, I went back to my room, the computer waiting for me. I was determined to complete the book and do justice to Len's work but I couldn't get motivated. I thought about my visit to Easter Island a tiny spec of land in a huge ocean, the sky full of dark grey, angry-looking clouds as I flew back out to Chile, the clouds reminded me of a story my father told me one night when I was about fifteen years old, he sat cross-legged in his tepee, breathing the smoke of white sage smudge sticks, it was a sacred day, he spoke of how the clouds in the sky can portray the future, that they are our guides. If we bother to follow the way we have been taught, we can see the future in clouds, the colour and their shape herald good fortune and warning signs alike.

He told me the clouds had fore-warned our ancestors that the white man was coming to steal their land and more importantly their heritage, which they did, then set about rubbing out our ancestors' history, describing them as nothing more than savages, they were ground into the dirt as if they had never existed. My father began smoking his ceremonial pipe, saying it bought him clarity and wisdom, saying, clouds never lie Red Feather, they return again and again, portrayed as fleeting shadows until the messages they bring us are understood. I wondered what point he was making. The white man he said looks on the ground for trails, footprints that lead to where animals and Indians might hide, to hunt them down. For many years the sky painted the colour of death, thousands of bison portrayed by clouds of dark grey, streaked with barbs of red scarring the sky, always travelling west, clouds like the bison fleeing the bullets of the white man's guns until the bison and Indians were no more. The sky was placid blue, serenely silent and empty, no wind, nor a cloud in sight, the day the United States of America was born. Years passed then yellow clouds began to appear to fill the empty sky, a signal that the stolen lands were to be ceded back to us as reservations where we might live in peace. My father said he was not taken with Reservations as a way to live and believed that at some time in the future, huge black clouds will fill the sky, their name unknown, he told me that on the appointed day the black clouds will drive the white man back to from whence they came in one mighty atomic storm and the sacred land that is currently called America will be returned to its rightful owners.

My father was smiling, a rare thing, he took my hand as he said:

"Red Feather, there are no numbers, no mathematical formulas in the sky or the Universe the white man speaks off, that can inform or confirm what we Indians have seen and already know. The clouds in the sky and the shadows that change the shape and colour of light are our guides and companions Red Feather. He let go of my hand and I felt dreadfully alone, where his words the ramblings of an embittered Indian warrior filled with hatred that had blinded him from all reason or was he describing the white Americans future, I was scared. When I had relayed the story to Len one night sitting on the balcony that overlooked the pyramids he said, "Yes I understand what your father was saying and trying to tell you, Henry." He smiled that gentle smile of his, but how could Len know?

Twenty-two

Arizona November 2012

The next day I was calmer and the recollection of cloud meanings put into perspective my father's concerns. I phoned him again saying the book was nearly finished and I was looking forward to coming home. He sounded pleased to hear my voice, he said something but I couldn't hear, I asked him if he was okay. He said yes then ended the call saying, "I am proud of you Red Feather."

For Len it didn't just rest there, there were other issues, groups of people whose abilities are also indefinable, Sharman, mediums, spirit guides, faith healers. People who do not fit into the academic notion of science or Charles Darwin's theories of natural evolution, neither do their paranormal abilities have a rational explanation. Len's research suggests there is a plausible explanation for Savants abilities, along with the mystics and mediums. Summarising some points made earlier. Len came to the conclusion that Science does not fully address 'the paranormal or unexplained'. In the 'bubble of rational' where many Scientists reside, they can only define and describe their knowledge with hard facts underpinned by mathematical equations, the foundation stones of their reason. Len was left with the frightening conclusion that some Scientists would rather have a wrong answer 'at any given time' than come to terms with the prospect that they have no explanation or answers to phenomena which do not have a quantifiable base, Len wrote:

Today the current scientific theory is the Universe is expanding some say to fast! but however hard the Scientist tries he cannot tell us what came before the 'big bang' and what the Universe is expanding into. Oddly they tell us they can predict how the Universe in billions of years to come will end perhaps without realising that ironically they are acting like seers, people who have no place in Science.

Leonardo Da Vinci has been credited as being a Polymath; to me, he is much more 'genius' than the word aims to describe him? In addition to his painting sculpting architectural, musical, scientific, mathematical and engineering skills our view was that he had the abilities of a Savant rather than those of a Polymath. Whatever titles are bestowed upon him this great man must rank as one of the most gifted of people who lived and in this now, PC correct world, bursting the concept that a person born out of wedlock might be at some disadvantage. You might have guessed he is a hero of mine. The work which caught my interest the most was his pencil drawing of 'The Vitruvian man' which illustrates the squaring of the circle. Da Vinci had a fascination for architecture and the value of proportion, his claim that 'man was God's greatest creation identified in the Vituravian Man with the proportions shown on the drawing. I had just been reviewing my research on Egyptology and the Pyramids in particular.

Len had drawn the proportions of the Great Pyramid and placed it over Leonardo's drawing to see if there was any correspondence between the two, unlike David Furlong's circles, unfortunately, there was no positive link. Len was first and foremost a mathematician. His short time in Egypt challenged every mathematical principle he had ever known, following his research and shortly before his death, his views changed in a subtle way to embrace a new mathematics that few fellow mathematicians would approve. 'Creationism' the Mathematics and Science of God, the Supreme Being.

On another scrap of paper I found in his bedside drawer he had written:

To my mind, the atheist provides endless hard facts that tell us, 'when we die, that's it, we are dead.' I believe these people, who keenly support Darwin's theory of mankind's evolution, live in a grey soulless world where there is supposedly an answer to everything, everything dies. By contrast, anyone who has witnessed the unique abilities of a Savant first-hand may come to the conclusion that their powers are supernatural, that numbers, theorems and equations are no more than the sum of knowledge of that which is known. But those who have read a poem or book, watched a play, film or the ballet, listened to the music of our great composers, operas and songs sung by a lone singer or the mighty choirs, looked at a painting or photograph will in some way have been moved by the essence of abstract thought, a moment locked and personified by time that reaches deep down within us, telling a story of our being, touching and feeding the soul that resides within us all. A DNA story within all of us, that unfolds into a belief that goes beyond science, mathematics and defies qualification.

Stories from, 'The path that has heart,' the path that through belief leads to 'God the Supreme Being? Where rather than dying, in God's world, everything lives through eternity, it's only the composition of our material being that changes and appears to die.

Len believed that whatever the mix of 'time, space, matter' and mankind's knowledge/interpretation of its material value, it is goodness and love that glues them together and makes sense of what we think, do and make. In the same way, it is evilness and hatred that smashes everything down impoverishing the soul, leaving us with a feeling of emptiness and a lack of belief. On the back of an envelope folded neatly in his diary written a few days before he died, Len had written with his fountain pen and favourite Prussian blue ink.

Passion, whether in the affirmative being love or in the negative being hate defies logic, description and explanation, though over many thousands of years much has been written on the subject. The emotions of love and hatred have huge power; they influence and constantly challenge our reason and actions. Perhaps that is what we define as the 'Human Condition'. Zen Buddhists desist from the hurly-burly of modern life, where experience is seen as necessary and to be crammed in, a notch on the bedpost, instead they seek spirituality by removing both emotions love and hate from their conscious, finding peace and tranquillity. Len had written in red ink:

This is a cop-out, adding,

The task for all of us in the short time we are alive on Earth is to deal with our own passions in a way that takes us forward towards fulfilment, <u>not to sit and meditate</u>.

He had underlined the end of the sentence.

This is why Don Juan's words had such significance when he said to me.

"Henry if you want something good to come out of your friend Len's life, if you believe in the eternal, life after death then it's very simple, 'follow the path that has heart.'" I was enamoured with Don Juan's words, there were ringing in my ears. I wanted to write them down, I remember looking around for something to write with, when I looked up again, Don Juan was gone. It was time for me to return home my mother and father would be waiting and also hopefully Shining eyes. I had completed Len's notes, made a CD and a hard copy sent separately to Len's father in Richmond, Surrey. I settled my account at the hotel and for the first time since Len's death, I felt good as I rode King from Phoenix, back to the homestead. As I approached the homestead, a mile out from the ridge I could just make out three people looking west towards me, my Mother my Father in his headdress and Shining eyes, they were waiting to greet me, having heard had heard the roar and vibration of Kings mighty engine, the white man's horse. I opened the throttle; I couldn't wait to be home.

Further Reading

A small selection of worldly books referred to in Len's Notes

Like stars, they twinkle with expectation. There are many more books on who are we, where did we come from and where are we going. The list is endless, mankind's thoughts that beg everlasting questions.

Carlos Castaneda	*The Teachings of Don Juan*
Jean Francois Champollion	*Grammaire Egyptienne My Journey to Egypt*
Michael Cordy	*The Colour of Death*
CW Ceram	*Gods, Graves and Scholars*
Leonardo Da Vinci	*The Notebooks of Leonardo Da Vinci*
Eric Von Daniken	*Chariots of the Gods*
Charles Darwin	*The Origins of The Species, Natural Selection*
Ignatius Donnelly	*Atlantis The Antediluvian World*
Paul Dirac	*Principles of Quantum Mathematics*
Albert Einstein	*Special Theory of Relativity, 'Invention is not the product of logical thought'*

Doctor Eberlin	*Foresight*
Robert Fitzroy	*Narrative of The Surveying of Voyages for His Majesty's Ship Adventure of The Beagle*
David Furlong	*The Keys to The Temple, Illuminating The Shadow*
Brian Greene	*The Elegant Universe*
Carl Fredrick Gauss	*The Theory of Motion, Disquisitions Arithmeticea*
John Gurdon	*Principles of Cloning*
Stephen Hawking	*The Universe in a Nutshell*
Thor Heyerdahl	*The Ra Expeditions*
Sir Fredrick Hoyle	*The Nature of The Universe*
HE Huntley	**The Faith of a Physicist**
John Hurchra	*Our Universe*
	The Guardians
Karl Jansky	*Star Noise*
Charles Lyell	**Principles of Geology**
Alan Lightman	*The Accidental Universe*
	Dance for 2
	Einstein's Dreams
James Lovelock	**The 'Gaia Theory'**
James Mac Donald	*The Legacy of Andre Celsius,*
Lynn Margulis	**The Journal of Theoretical Biology 'Symbiosis in cell evolution'**
Jon Michell	*View over Atlantis*

Sir Isaac Newton	*The Principia*
	The Emerald Tablet
	The Chronology of Ancient Kingdoms Amended
Kim and Fran Peek	*The Real Rain Man*
Lynn Pickett Clive Prince	*The Stargate conspiracy*
Rand Flem-ath & Colin Wilson	*The Atlantis Blueprint*
Claudius James Rich	*Narrative of a journey to the site of Babylon*
Karl Sabbagh	*Dr Riemann's Zeros*
Henrick Schliemann	*Troy and Its Remains*
Mary Shelly	*Frankenstein*
	The Last Man
Bryan Sykes	*Cheddar Man*
	The Seven Daughters of Eve
	The Human Inheritance
Daniel Tammet	*Born on a blue day*
	Thinking in Numbers
Darold Treffert	*Islands of Genius*
Immanuel Velikovsky	**Worlds in Collision**
Alfred Wallace	*Natural Selection*
	Beyond, The Malay Archipelago
EA Wallis Budge	*The Book of The Dead*
Alfred Watkins	*The Old Straight track*

HG Wells	*God the Invisible King*
	A Modern Utopia
	The War Of The Worlds
	The Time Machine
	The Outline Of History
Christopher Wills	*The Runaway Brain*
	The Spark of Life
Stephen Wiltshire	*Biography*

Acknowledgement

I wish to thank my wife, Angela for the assistance she has gave me and without whose help the novel would not have seen the light of day.

About the Author

I was a "war baby", my mother Nora Donnelly had a brief romance with Donald Ettinger an American GI. I was born in a private nursing home in a place called East Sheen close to Kew Gardens on the 1st of September 1944, the name on my birth certificate read Michael Roy Donnelly, father unknown.

Sometime in 1944, my father was posted to Europe and in 1945 returned to America, not England to my mother's surprise. I grew up not knowing my father, it is fair to say that he may not have known of my existence. I was known as Michael Ettinger at kindergarten and my name was formally changed by deed poll to Michael Roy Donnelly Ettinger to coincide with a second baptism and first communion when I was seven years old.

Unsurprisingly I was an immature and shy child, my saving grace after a short spell in a foster home was that I was brought up by my Grandmother, whilst my mother who lived with us went to work. I used to call my grandmother Mum, it was not until I was nineteen and ready to marry that I was told by my Uncle Ted that Nora was my real mother, funnily she had also changed her name from Donnelly to Ettinger, when I was about 12, though she never told me why. In many ways none of this mattered, though I never liked having to explain about my father when asked, like everyone else I got on with my life, it was only much later at the age of 64, from one email sent on the spur of the moment through cyberspace to a man I had never met in St George Utah that everything changed.

Unbelievably I had traced my father and discovered that I had three brothers and two sisters, alas, I was unable to meet Abby the older sister who had died. My father Donald Ettinger known in the American football annuals as "Red Dog" had come into my life, though like Abby he had died before I was able to meet him, he was very much alive to me. So too were my three wonderful brothers and surviving sister who treated me like I had always been part of their family, "a story in itself". Ever since I can remember I had yearned to visit America, to become an "American Citizen" I always felt American, it was my birthright, something that had been denied as I lived my life in England. It wasn't that I was unhappy, it was just that something had always been missing, an empty space inside of me, waiting to be filled.

The irony of my mother changing my name from

Donnelly to Ettinger was that it became the key to finding my family in America. The icing on the cake was being granted American Citizenship some 18 months later.

I love England and Yorkshire where I live with my wife, Angela, I am proud to be British, but my heart and soul belong to America, eight short years ago, unplanned a dream came true. Now I feel I belong. I have found my roots, the love of my brothers and sister and have an American identity, it is a wonderful feeling that words can never properly describe.

Available worldwide from
Amazon and all good bookstores

———————

For further information, please contact the Author
ettinger@talktalk.net

———————

www.mtp.agency

www.facebook.com/mtp.agency

@mtp_agency